MANUAL FOR WINSTON ADVANCED GRAMMAR PROGRAM

INTRODUCTION

The purposes of the Winston Advanced Grammar Program are to:

1. **Review** parts of speech, noun functions, prepositional phrases, and modification for students in upper elementary grades, secondary school, and college in a thorough, pleasant, and successful manner.

2. **Continue grammar study** with the introduction of possessive forms, various pronouns, verbals, and clauses.

3. **Promote positive feelings of success** in this often troublesome subject.

4. **Provide teachers with materials** and procedures for fostering interest in traditional English grammar and other language learning areas.

5. **Encourage total student participation** in every aspect of classroom activity.

6. **Suggest activities** different from those found in traditional textbooks.

7. **Provide foreign language teachers with a method to review** principles of English grammar.

8. **Provide instruments to assess student knowledge** of grammar concepts.

For the teacher who has not used the Basic Level Winston Grammar Program

Basic Winston Grammar covers the following subjects: Articles, nouns, pronouns, verbs, contractions, adjectives, adverbs, prepositional phrases, coordinating conjunctions, interjections, ellipses, subjects, direct and indirect objects, predicate nominatives, nouns of direct address, and appositives. If your student doesn't have a good grasp of these concepts, then the Advanced Grammar will be difficult and frustrating. The review test at the beginning of the book should be given to ascertain any areas that need special review. Worksheets 31-40 are designed for review purposes. If, after finishing those worksheets, the student is still having difficulty, it would be reasonable to obtain the Basic Level Winston Grammar and do some in-depth review. In the Basic Program, each part of speech is on a color-coded card. There are enough cards so that the student may put down one card for each word in the sentence. A plain black card indicates any word that has not been covered to that point in the program. By the completion of the Basic Program, there are no black cards used in any sentence. Most students have all the cards memorized so that they no longer need to put down a card for every word, but will often use them for reference. For this reason, the Advanced Program includes only one each of the small parts of speech cards from the Basic Program plus several extra that will be new to the Advanced Program. The large cards, numbered 1- 8, are also introduced in the Basic Program. They indicate the order in which the nouns in a sentence can be successfully decoded. Most students, having completed the Basic Program, will have this process memorized. If you have not used the Basic Level, it will be important to follow the sequence every time at the beginning of the Advanced Program to firmly fix it in the student's mind. The other extra large cards will be introduced in the Advanced Program.

It is always a better plan to break up each worksheet into at least 2 - 3 days work. Every time a student comes back to a worksheet, he/she will have to mentally review the concept, which will solidify it faster. Before moving on to the next worksheet, a good idea would be to spend a day or two finding that particular concept in some reading material and also to practice using the concept in his/her own writing. If at all possible, have the student do this in some already assigned report rather than making a special writing assignment just for grammar. Students need to see that grammar concepts are needed in every piece of writing, from science to history to literature, even math word problems. If you have any further questions, or need more information, feel free to contact us.

ADVANCED WINSTON GRAMMAR PROGRAM SEQUENCE OF TOPICS

Worksheet No.	Topic
	REVIEW TEST
31-35	Review--Parts of Speech
36-40	Review--Noun Functions
41	Possessive Adjectives
42, 43	Possessive Pronouns, Nouns, and Adjectives
44, 45	Possessive Nouns
46-48	Pronouns and Adjectives
49	Reflexives
50-52	Interrogative Pronouns
	QUIZ
53-55	Present Participles
56	Past Participles
57	Present and Past Participles
58	Correlative Conjunctions
59, 60	Simple Infinitives
61, 62	Simple Gerunds
	QUIZ
63, 64	Subject-Verb Combinations
65, 66	Clause Identification
67, 68	Adverb Clauses
69, 70	Compound Sentences
71	Complex Sentences
	QUIZ
72, 73	Relative Pronouns and Adjective Clauses
74, 75	Ellipsed Relative Pronouns and Embedded Clauses
	QUIZ
76, 77	Noun Clauses as Direct Objects
78	Noun Clauses as Indirect Objects
79	Noun Clauses as Predicate Nominatives
	QUIZ
80	Noun Clauses as Objects of Prepositions
81	Noun Clauses as Appositives
82	Noun Clauses as Subjects
83-85	Clause Practice
	POST TEST

REVIEW TEST

Teachers should administer the Review Test before starting Advanced Grammar.

Results of this test indicate mastery of parts of speech, noun functions, and prepositional phrases.

Advanced Grammar assumes that students have a firm grasp of these grammar concepts.

Exercises 31-40 provide review of these concepts. It is conceivable, however, that students scoring at mastery level on the Review Test could go directly to Worksheet 41.

Key to the **Review Test** follows.

1.	not, very	16.	is, am
2.	in the corner	17.	two (Sal, I)
3.	chair	18.	student
4.	chair	19.	excellent
5.	isn't	20.	an
6.	(you)	21.	to Yale
7.	coins	22.	went
8.	adverb	23.	Mr. Porter
9.	Take	24.	principal
10.	Bob	25.	two (Mr. Porter, Yale)
11.	have	26.	Tom
12.	Bob	27.	adverb
13.	two (She, I)	28.	returned
14.	and	29.	Golly
15.	adjective	30.	two (book, it)

(Score one point for each question, total 30)

Directions for Worksheets 31-35

Worksheets 31-35 provide review of parts of speech. Students may use the nine parts-of-speech cards for reference. They do not have to put cards down in sequence for each sentence. Students can just keep cards handy for reference.

Proceed to Worksheets 31-35.

Directions for Worksheets 36-40

The next five worksheets in Advanced Grammar provide review/practice in identifying nouns and pronouns, and the functions they perform. It is essential that students can readily assign functions to all nouns and pronouns before proceeding in the program.

Distribute Cards 1-8. The smaller noun card (white) and pronoun card (gray) may also be used as references while students identify nouns and pronouns in the sentences on Worksheets 36-40. Only nouns and pronouns are to be marked on these next five worksheets. Underline nouns; write pron. over personal pronouns. Then assign a function to each, using the process of elimination featured by the noun function cards.
EVERY NOUN AND EVERY PRONOUN PERFORMS A NOUN FUNCTION!

Note: Review noun function definitions from The Basic Level Winston Grammar Teacher's Manual, pages 53-69.

Write **S** over each subject. Determine whether the main verb is an action or linking verb. Then mark functions as indicated on the noun function cards:

    Circle direct objects
    Box indirect objects
    Write **O.P.** over objects of prepositions
    Write **P.N.** over predicate nominatives
    Write **APP.** over appositives
    Write **N.D.A.** above nouns of direct address.

Proceed with Worksheets 36-40.

Directions for Worksheet 41

Each student receives one possessive adjective card.   These orange cards are bordered in blue.

my	our
your	your
her	their
(his)	
its	it's = it is
	~~its~~

Possessive adjectives always come before nouns. They tell whose (noun). His is in parentheses because it can also be a possessive **pronoun**. This may be confusing.

If **his** comes before a noun and answers, "Whose (noun)?" it is an adjective.
If it performs a noun function, it is a pronoun. Students
will practice at distinguishing these concepts on Worksheet 42.
Worksheet 41 shows **his** only as an adjective.

Its' is included on the card, and students are instructed to notice that it is **crossed out**. We hope this will eventually extinguish its use. **No such word exists.**
It's is not an adjective-it is a contraction of **it is**.

The reverse side of the possessive adjective card indicates that these words are annotated in exactly the same manner as other adjectives, except that they never modify pronouns.

The slender woman returned my smile.

Note: Again, students do not have to distinguish the possessive adjective his
from the possessive pronoun until Worksheet 42. Worksheet 41 employs
this word only as an adjective.

Sentences for class presentation:

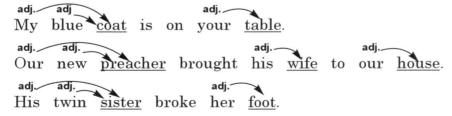

My blue coat is on your table.

Our new preacher brought his wife to our house.

His twin sister broke her foot.

Proceed to Worksheet 41.

Directions for Worksheets 42 and 43

Distribute one possessive pronoun card to each student. This is a small gray card with a red border. **All possessive pronouns perform noun functions.** Students may refer to this card as they do to the others.

The possessive pronouns are:

mine	ours
yours	yours
hers	theirs
(his)	

Note: **His** is in parentheses. **His** is often an adjective. . . **his** coat. Students need to practice deciding whether **his** is being used as a possessive pronoun or an adjective. If it comes before a noun and tells, "Whose coat?", it is an adjective. If **his** performs a noun function, it is a possessive pronoun.

Preliminary practice:

On the board or overhead projector, give students these sample sentences.

> Mine is red, and his is green.
> (**His** is a possessive pronoun in this sentence because it does not come before a noun, and it is the subject of the verb **is**.)

> His will be ready in a few minutes.
> (His is the subject of the verb phrase **will be**; it is a possessive pronoun.)

> He forgot his watch.
> (**His** is an adjective. Which (or whose) watch? (**His** does *not* perform a noun function in this sentence.)

Note: **Its** is so rarely used as a possessive pronoun that it is not included on the possessive pronoun card.

Proceed to Worksheets 42 and 43.

NOTES

7

Directions for Worksheet 44

Students should be comfortable with all noun functions, possessive adjectives, and possessive pronouns.

Worksheet 44 introduces possessive adjectives formed from words that normally function as nouns.

  1. Tom's book is red.

     adj. (book)
  2. Tom's is red.

In Sentence 1, Tom's modifies book. Adjectives modify nouns. We prefer to refer to Tom's as an adjective since its function is to modify book.

In Sentence 2, Tom's is also an adjective. The noun it modifies is not expressed, so we insert it. If no antecedent is provided, insert an "X."

  adj. (X)
  Mom's is the best.

When a possessive form of a word modifies a noun, expressed or unexpressed, it is an adjective.

Review: Singular nouns form possessives with 's. Plural nouns ending in **s** are spelled by adding a final '.

Consult a dictionary appendix for some exceptions and options:

  Children's   Charles' **or** Charles's   Men's

A few indefinite pronouns form possessives. We will take this up later.

Sentences for classroom presentation:

  adj.
  Mike's book is not here.

  adj.
  The teachers' room is open.
  (Which room? Teachers' room. Teachers' is an adjective.)

  adj.   *adj.* (team)
  Barry's team won, but Ted's lost.

  adj. (X)
  Mary's is on the porch.

Proceed with Worksheet 44.

Directions for Worksheet 45

Worksheet 45 continues to provide practice in identifying possessives that perform noun functions. Several of the sentences will be challenging to students . . . and maybe all of us!

Proceed to Worksheet 45.

NOTES

Directions for Worksheets 46, 47, 48

Distinguishing Adjectives from Pronouns

Many words act as either pronouns or adjectives. It is essential that students learn to differentiate these uses in sentences before trying to analyze sentence parts.

Worksheets 46, 47, and 48 introduce students to the task of deciding whether a particular word performs a noun function, and is, therefore, a pronoun, or modifies a noun, and is, therefore, an adjective.

Example:

       S
     pron.
That is my coat.

  adj.
That <u>coat</u> is mine.

In the first sentence, **that** is the subject of the linking verb, **is. That** is an adjective in the second sentence. It modifies the noun **coat**.

The categories of words which often act as pronouns, but can also be used as adjectives are:

> Demonstrative pronouns (this, that, etc.)
> Interrogative pronouns (which, what, etc.)
> Indefinite pronouns (few, some, etc.)

The ability to identify noun functions is a key factor when identifying a word as a pronoun or adjective. If a word performs a noun function and is not a noun, it must (at this point) be identified as a pronoun.

If the word in question is not performing a noun function, but modifying a noun, it is an adjective. These adjectives do not conform to the definition we have learned except that they answer the adjective questions. They **cannot** come between articles and nouns. They usually do not have antonyms.

Distribute the small gray card with the blue border. Students add this card to the reference deck. The clue side of the card shows seven words that are often troublesome. The reverse side of the card shows students how to determine their parts of speech in a given sentence.

If the word in question (represented by an *****) appears before a noun, it is an adjective. If the word performs a noun function, it is a pronoun.

Note: The third clue will be helpful later, when clauses are introduced. Disregard it for now.

A list of words students must identify as adjectives or pronouns follows.

This	that	these	those	which
whose	what	all	any	another
anyone	both	each	either	everybody
everyone	few	many	most	neither
nobody	none	some	other	several
somebody	someone	something	one, two, three...	

Sentences for class discussion:

<pre>
       S   S
     pron.   c.c.   pron.
Many <u>apply</u>, but few <u>are</u> <u>chosen</u>.
</pre>

Many is a pronoun because it is not a noun, but it performs a noun function (subject of **apply**).

Few is a pronoun. It is not a noun. It performs a noun function (subject of **are chosen**).

<pre>
    adj.   S   c.c.   adj.   S
Many <u>teenagers</u> <u>apply</u>, but few <u>girls</u> <u>are</u> <u>chosen</u>.
</pre>

Many is an adjective. It does not perform a noun function; it modifies **teenagers** (how many?).

Few is an adjective. "How many girls?" Few **girls**.

<pre>
   S   O.P.
 Pron. prep. pron.   prep. O.P.
One (of them) <u>will</u> <u>be</u> (in jail.)
</pre>

One is a pronoun because it performs a noun function.   It is the subject of **will be**.

<pre>
   adj.   S   prep. O.P.
One <u>boy</u> <u>will</u> <u>be</u> (in jail.)
</pre>

One is an adjective modifying boy.

Distribute a **Tricky Words** card and **Tricky Word Clues** card to the deck of noun function cards. The new cards help students to determine the parts of speech of puzzling words.

When the student encounters a word which does not readily comply with the rules, he can look it up to see what it might be.

Example:

Most of the food is delicious.

If the student is confused about **most**, he looks it up on the **Tricky Words** card. There he learns that **most** can be an adjective or a pronoun. The student then refers to the **Tricky Word Clues** card. There he is reminded that, if the word is an adjective, it will be modifying a noun or pronoun. If **most** is a pronoun, it will be performing a noun function.

The student then determines that in the sentence:

    S   prep. ✓   O.P.   adj.
Most (of the <u>food</u>) <u>is</u> delicious.

Most is the subject. Since the subject is a noun function, **most** must be a pronoun. (**Most** is not a noun because it cannot form a plural, nor can it follow the article **the** in this context.)

Note: Some references on the Tricky Words card have not yet been covered.
      Tell students to ignore them until they are introduced in subsequent lessons.

Proceed to Worksheets 46-48.

NOTES

Directions for
Worksheet 49

Worksheet 49 involves reflexive pronouns. It also presents the first **major** departure from rules learned in previous lessons.

Rule for memorization:

Words ending in **-self** or **-selves** are (reflexive) pronouns. Mark them **pron.**

Note: Many grammar programs differentiate reflexive pronouns according to their functions as pronouns, intensifiers, or even adverbs. The reflexive form is used in these three constructions:

He shot himself in the foot. (**noun function**)
The expert himself was puzzled. (**intensification**)
We did it ourselves. (**adverbial**)

We prefer simply to mark all reflexive forms as pronouns and discuss these different constructions. Most students are confident of their mastery to date, and can accept the notion that pronouns can act as adverbs or intensifiers.

Sentence for class discussion:

She gave herself a rest from housework today.

Herself ends in **self**: it is therefore a pronoun. It performs a noun function-- indirect object.

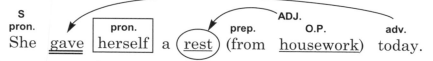

Another sentence for class discussion:

A sentence using a reflexive as an intensifier:

The teacher herself couldn't find the answer.

In the sentence above, **herself** performs no noun function. We mark it **pron.** A case can be made that **herself** is an adverb. It can be moved.

The teacher couldn't find the answer **herself**.

13

However, the meaning of the sentence has subtly changed; the intended meaning of the sentence implies that the answer was too difficult to find. The students should not be expected to find it. After all, even the teacher had difficulty. If we move **herself** to the end of the sentence, the meaning possibly shifts to the sense that the teacher is in the library asking the librarian for assistance.

Sentence for class discussion:

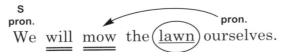

Here we see the violation mentioned earlier. A pronoun *modifying a verb?* **Ourselves** obviously modifies **mow**. "Mow how?" While teachers might prefer to annotate this construction by marking **ourselves** "adv.," we prefer to mark all words ending in **-self** or **-selves** as pronouns.

Discuss this issue openly, and come to an understanding with students. Teacher preference should determine how your class handles the problem.

Proceed to worksheet 49.

NOTES

Directions for
Worksheets 50 and 51

Worksheets 50 and 51 introduce **interrogative pronouns**. They also review other pronoun forms.

Rule for memorization:

> **Who, whom, which, what, whose** are often pronouns when they introduce questions. They are sometimes direct objects in these sentences.

Note: Sentences in question form **often** reverse the normal order of words. Students should be alerted to this possibility. Have students rearrange all questions as statements before performing their analyses.

> Who is the teacher?
> The teacher is who.
>
> What can we take?
> We can take what.
>
> Whom can I trust?
> I can trust whom.

Students should take care not to identify these words as pronouns unless they perform noun functions. Some of these words are often adjectives.

> adj.
> Which boy won the race?
>
> adj.
> Whose house is on the corner?

Notice that sentence order **is not inverted** in the constructions above.

> adj.
> Which car will we take?
>
> adj.
> What decision did they reach?

Notice that sentence order is inverted in the constructions above.

Note: While students resist the proper use of **whom** as an objective pronoun, it is appropriate to make this point now. Once the noun function of who/whom is determined, the following rule can be observed:

> **Whom** is the proper form if the noun function in question is a direct object, indirect object, or object of a preposition. Otherwise, use **who**.

Examples for classroom discussion:

Who/Whom did you see on the stairs?

You did see (whom) on the stairs.

With **who/whom** did you play?

O.P.
You did play (with whom?)

This usage principle is practiced in later exercises.

Proceed to Worksheets 50 and 51.

Directions for Worksheet 52

Simple sentences in question form often begin with interrogative adverbs.

where   why   when   how

While these words will perform more complicated functions later, Worksheet 52 gives students practice in identifying them as simple adverbs.

Sentence for class presentation:

When will we see Grandmother?

Proceed to Worksheet 52.

Note: A quiz follows Worksheet 52.

NOTES

Directions for Worksheets 53-55

The issue of simple present participial forms of verbs has not been addressed. Worksheets 53-55 give students practice recognizing these forms and deciding whether they are parts of verbs or adjectives.

Rule for memorization: If a verb ends in **-ing** and comes after a helping verb, it is probably part of the verb. If it modifies a noun, it is an adjective.

Sentences for class presentation:

    S   ADV.
  pron.   prep. O.P.
  I am going (to church.)

Going follows a helping verb. It is part of the verb.

  S
  pron.
  We are collecting (butterflies.)

Collecting follows the helping verb **are**. It is a verb.

                          ADV.
 ✓   adj.   S   prep.   O.P.
 The exciting game lasted (until midnight.)

Exciting comes between the article **the** and the noun **game**. Which game? It has an antonym (dull). **Exciting** is an adjective.

   ✓   S   adj.
  The problem is confusing.

This construction is tricky. If we consider **confusing** to be a verb, the sentence is quite awkward. Further study shows us that **confusing** is an adjective modifying **problem**. More sentences for class presentation:

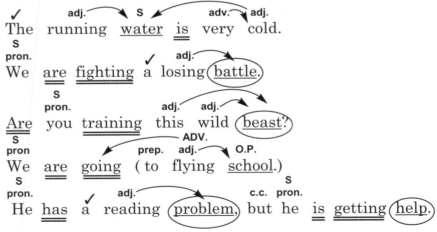

Proceed to Worksheets 53-55.

Directions for Worksheet 56

Past participles, as parts of verbs, have been covered. Worksheet 56 helps students to identify their use as simple adjectives. Like present participles, these verb forms will follow rules for either verbs **or** adjectives. If a past participle modifies a noun or pronoun, mark it as an adjective.

Sentences for class presentation:

    The lost **child** found his mother.

    The <u>child</u> <u>was</u> <u>burned</u> on the hand.

    A frozen **pond** attracts skaters.

    The <u>lamp</u> <u>is</u> <u>lit</u> every night.

    The cleaned <u>fish</u> <u>were</u> <u>put</u> in the oven.

    The <u>books</u> <u>are</u> <u>checked</u> by the teacher.

If a simple past participle in a sentence seems to fit between an article and a noun **without disrupting the meaning** of the sentence, it is an adjective.

    The shoe is ripped.   The ripped shoe...

    The dog is trained.   The trained dog...

    The chair <u>is</u> <u>turned</u> to the wall.

    A woman <u>is</u> <u>expected</u> to win the election.

It does not make sense to say:

    The turned chair is to the wall.

    An expected woman is to win the election.

Note: In some sentences, the differences are very subtle. The teacher is encouraged to accept **either** interpretation from the student as long as he can demonstrate understanding of his response.

Proceed to Worksheet 56.

Directions for Worksheet 57

Worksheet 57 mixes simple present and simple past participial forms of verbs. Students are required to discern whether these words act as verbs or adjectives.

Proceed to Worksheet 57.

Directions for Worksheet 58

Students have learned the common coordinating conjunctions:

and   **but**   **for**   **yet**   **or**   **nor**   **;**

Worksheet 58 covers correlative conjunctions. Correlative conjunctions are marked **c.c.**, just as coordinating conjunctions. Correlatives are merely pairs of conjunctions which link grammatical units.

    both . . . . and
    not only. . . . . . .but also
    either. . . . . . . .or
    neither. . . . . . .nor

Sentences for class discussion:

    c.c.   S   c.c. pron.   P.N.
    Both John and I are Democrats.

    c.c.   c.c.   pron.   c.c. pron. c.c.   pron. prep. O.P.
    Not   only   did we   win, but   we   also   did   it   (with   style!)

    c.c.   pron.   c.c. pron.
    Either you go, or I will call Dad.

    pron.   c.c.   adj.   c.c.   adj.
    We   desire   neither   your   money   nor   your   land.

Proceed with worksheet 58.

19

Directions for Worksheets 59 and 60

Simple infinitives are introduced on Worksheets 59 and 60.

Rule for memorization:

An infinitive is a verb form composed of the word **to** plus a verb. Infinitives act as nouns, adjectives, and adverbs. We put parentheses around infinitives and mark them for part of speech and function.

Sentences for class discussion:

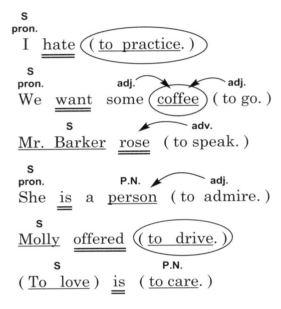

Worksheets 59 and 60 provide students with practice recognizing simple infinitives. Remind students that the word **to** often indicates an infinitive, but it can be a preposition. **To** is in parenthesis on the preposition card. Now students will have to identify whether it is part of an infinitive or a preposition.

Distribute the verbal card (white with blue border).

Proceed to Worksheets 59 and 60.

NOTES

Directions for Worksheets 61 and 62

Worksheets 61 and 62 introduce **simple gerunds**. Gerunds are verbs ending in **-ing** which act as nouns. They differ from nouns in that they usually do not form plurals, and they are often awkward when tested with the article **the**.

Students identify gerunds with the following rule for memorization:

Gerunds are **-ing** forms of verbs which perform noun functions. We underline gerunds and identify their noun functions.

Sentences for class presentation:

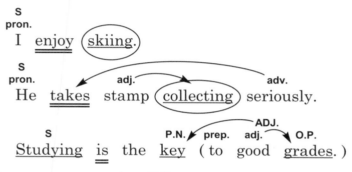

Students must practice differentiating gerunds from verbs and participles (adjectives). **The key to identifying gerunds is the fact that they perform noun functions.**

More sentences for class presentation:

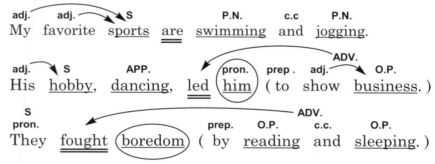

Note: A cumulative quiz follows Worksheet 62.

Proceed to Worksheets 61 and 62.

Directions for Worksheets 63 and 64

Thus far in the program, students have been exposed to uncomplicated sentence constructions. The remainder of Advanced Grammar teaches identification of independent and dependent clauses.

The key to identifying clauses is the accurate counting of subject-verb combinations.

Simple subject-verb combinations:

    ^s
I go.

       ^s
John writes.

           ^s
The gorilla roars.

Every clause, independent or dependent, has its own subject-verb combination. Count the subject-verb combinations in the sentences below.

       ^s   ^s
John slept, but Sid read a book.   (2)

       ^s
Peter can't be in the play.   (1)

         ^s
The pony threw the rider.   (1)

     ^s   ^s
They left, and we cleaned up.   (2)

     ^s   ^s
Can you wait while Jack writes a check?   (2)

It gets more complicated if we use compound subjects and/or compound verbs.

       ^s   ^s
The boys and girls sat on opposite sides.   (1)

Rule for memorization:

Compound subjects and/or compound verbs belong to the **same** subject-verb combination.

Count the subject-verb combinations in the following sentences for class presentation:

    ^s   ^s

Mother and I <u>plowed</u> the garden.   (1)

  ^s

She <u>sewed</u> and <u>ironed</u> our costumes.   (1)

  ^s   ^s

Billy and Tom <u>talked</u> and <u>talked</u>.   (1)

  ^s   ^s

They and we <u>argued</u> and <u>discussed</u> the issues.   (1)

  ^s   ^s

You <u>will</u>, but I <u>won't</u>.   (2)

The lines above are marked as follows: "s" over the subjects and underlines under the verbs.

Note that in the last example, the coordinating conjunction forms neither a compound subject nor a compound verb.

More sentences for class presentation:

  ^s
  (You)

<u>Find</u> and <u>arrest</u> the robbers.   (1)

  ^s   ^s

Zoos and parks <u>are</u> <u>managed</u> by the City Council.   (1)

  ^s   ^s

You <u>wash</u>, and I'<u>ll</u> <u>dry</u>   (2)

  ^s   ^s

He'<u>s</u> a doctor, yet he <u>smokes</u>.   (2)

  ^s   ^s

She <u>can</u> <u>be</u> calm, but she often <u>yells</u> and <u>screams</u>.   (2)

Worksheets 63 and 64 present students with the task of counting subject-verb combinations.

Proceed to Worksheets 63 and 64.

NOTES

Directions for Worksheets 65 and 66

Worksheets 65 and 66 provide practice with clause identification.

Rule for memorization:

> Each subject-verb combination indicates the presence of a clause in a sentence. Put brackets around clauses.

Definition for memorization:

> A clause is a group of words that includes a subject and a verb.
> (Note: this definition will be expanded later.)

Sentence for class presentation:

> Bob slept while Mary worked.

There are **two** subject-verb combinations in this sentence; there are **two** clauses.

>   s   s
> [Bob slept] [while Mary worked.]   (2)

At first, sentences for class discussion will be kept very simple, leaving students and teacher only the decision, "Where should we split the clauses?"

In the sentence above, students will sense that **while** belongs with the subject-verb combination **Mary worked**.

Sentences for class presentation:

>   s   s
> [The trumpet blared] [as the cymbals clashed.]   (2)
>
>   s   s
> [Before I could call him] [he was out the door.]   (2)
>
>   s   s
> [When they arrived,] [they appeared tired.]   (2)
>
>   s
> [(You)   s
>   Wait] [until we decide.]   (2)
>
>   s   s
> [We can go] [if our work is done.]   (2)

Worksheets 65 and 66 require students to count subject-verb combinations and bracket clauses.

Proceed to Worksheets 65 and 66.

24

Directions for Worksheets 67 and 68

Students should be able to identify the clauses in a complex sentence containing one independent and one dependent clause. Worksheet 69 provides practice with differentiating the independent clause from the dependent clause.

Note: Students will be working with the complex sentence before the compound sentence. Identifying the adverb clause has proven to be the most effective way to teach the principle that clauses can be parts of speech.

Rule for memorization:

If a clause can stand alone, it is an **independent** clause. If it does not sound complete, it is a **dependent** clause. Dependent clauses act as parts of speech.

The first dependent clauses we will deal with are **adverb** clauses. Like adverbs, adverb clauses modify verbs, adjectives, or other adverbs. Also, most adverb clauses can be moved to another spot in the sentence. Adverb clauses answer the questions on the adverb card.

Rule for memorization:

The first word in an adverb clause is a subordinating conjunction.
Mark it with **S.C.**

Worksheets 67 and 68 require students to:

1. Count subject-verb combinations
2. Bracket clauses
3. Identify **dependent** clauses
4. Indicate what they modify
5. Mark subordinating conjunctions with **S.C.**

Sentence for class presentation:

ADV.
S.C.
[As Tom practiced,] [the teacher took notes.]   1 ②) 3

As Tom practiced does not "sound complete." It is a dependent clause.
As Tom practiced can be moved to the end of the sentence.
As Tom practiced modifies took -"took when?"

More sentences for class presentation:

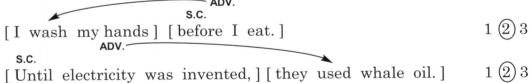

ADV.
S.C.
[I wash my hands] [before I eat.]   1 ②) 3

ADV.
S.C.
[Until electricity was invented,] [they used whale oil.]   1 ②) 3

25

Directions for Worksheets 69 and 70

Students should be comfortable with complex sentences containing one adverb clause. Worksheets 69 and 70 introduce compound sentences containing two or more independent clauses.

Rule for memorization:

> An independent clause is a group of words which can stand alone. When a coordinating conjunction links two clauses, it is outside both brackets.
>
> [She is nice,] but [he is nasty.]
>
> **Independent clauses do not act as parts of speech.**

Worksheets 69 and 70 require students to count subject-verb combinations, identify all clauses, and mark adverb clauses and subordinating conjunctions.

Sentence for class presentation:

ADV.
S.C.   S   S
[While I recovered,] [Mother took my paper route.]   1 ②3

More sentences for class presentation:

[Jan is bright,] yet [she gets poor grades.]   1 ②3

ADV.
S.C.
[Until I return,] [you may watch T.V.]   1 ②3

ADV.
S.C.
[As the storm continued,] [we piled the sand bags.]   1 ②3

ADV.
S.C.
[Bob sulked about it] ; [we ignored him] [as we had before.]   1 2 ③

Note: Students should be comfortable enough with clause identification that they no longer need to mark subjects and verbs.

Proceed to Worksheets 69 and 70.

NOTES

26

Directions for Worksheet 71

Worksheet 71 continues with compound independent clauses and introduces sentences with more than one adverb clause.

Sentences for class presentation:

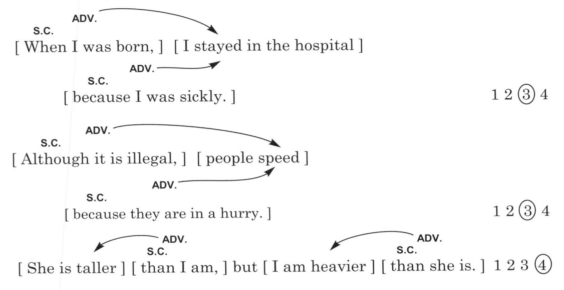

[When I was born,] [I stayed in the hospital]

[because I was sickly.]   1 2 ③ 4

[Although it is illegal,] [people speed]

[because they are in a hurry.]   1 2 ③ 4

[She is taller] [than I am,] but [I am heavier] [than she is.] 1 2 3 ④

A cumulative quiz follows Worksheet 71.

Proceed to Worksheet 71.

NOTES

27

Directions for Worksheets 72 and 73

Worksheets 72 and 73 introduce adjective clauses. Adjective clauses begin with relative pronouns, and they modify nouns and (rarely) pronouns. **The noun modified by the adjective clause is almost always directly in front of the adjective clause.**

The common relative pronouns are:

who (ever)	which (ever)	that
whose	whom (ever)	why
where	what (ever)	how

Students should count subject-verb combinations and identify dependent clauses. Adjective clauses begin with relative pronouns. Put **R.P.** over relative pronouns and draw arrows to nouns or pronouns modified.

Sentences for class presentation:

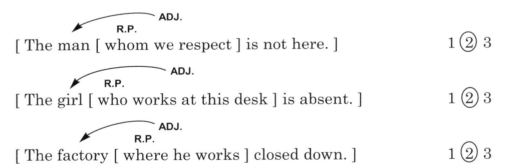

Note: Adjective clauses are often embedded inside independent clauses. Sometimes a R.P. can also act as the subject of the clause as in the second example.

Note: Only adjective and adverb dependent clauses appear on Worksheets 72 and 73.

If a dependent clause can be moved, it is most likely an adverb clause.

Proceed to Worksheets 72 and 73.

Directions for Worksheets 74 and 75

Many times the relative pronouns **that, who**, and **whom** are not expressed in a sentence, but understood. This ellipsis is very common in everyday language.

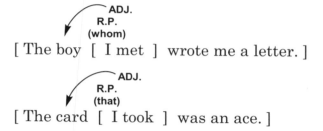

[The boy [I met] wrote me a letter.]

[The card [I took] was an ace.]

Students should add the missing relative pronoun where it would normally appear.

Worksheets 74 and 75 include sentences containing ellipsed relative pronouns.

Note: A cumulative quiz follows Worksheet 75.

NOTES

Directions for Worksheets 76 and 77

Students should be comfortable recognizing adverb and adjective clauses. A review of relative pronouns (Worksheet directions for 72 and 73) is helpful at this point.

Relative pronouns introduce not only adjective clauses but also noun clauses.

Rule for memorization:

> A dependent clause introduced by a relative pronoun is either an adjective clause or a noun clause. If the clause performs a noun function, it is a **noun clause**. If the clause modifies a noun, it is an **adjective clause**.

Note: Worksheets 76-82 introduce noun clauses in a controlled sequence. Worksheets 76 and 77 contain only adverb clauses, adjective clauses, and noun clauses acting as **direct objects**.

Helpful Clue: Adjective clauses usually appear directly after a noun.

R.P.   ADJ.
The man [who came to dinner]. . .

ADJ.
R.P.
(that)
The one [I want] . . .

Emphasize:

> **Noun clauses are introduced by relative pronouns, and they perform noun functions.**

Below are sentences for classroom presentation that contain adjective clauses, adverb clauses, and noun clauses acting as direct objects. Students may now **stop** bracketing independent clauses. Identify **only** dependent clauses.

R.P.
I know ([what you want.])   1 ② 3

R.P.
She wants ([whatever you can afford.])   1 ② 3

R.P.
I wonder ([whom I can ask.])   1 ② 3

ADJ.   ADV.
R.P.   S.C.
(that)
That is the story [we read] [when I was a boy.]   1 2 ③

30

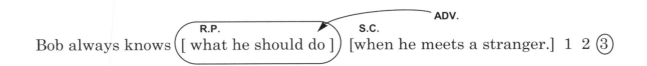

Bob always knows ([what he should do]) [when he meets a stranger.] 1 2 ③

Additional help for Worksheet 76:

Remember that words such as **whose, whatever**, or **whichever** only function as relative pronouns if they fill that function in a dependent clause. (Reminder: Clauses must have a subject and a verb.) Sometimes these words act as adjectives and modify the noun they are next to.

Sentences for class presentation:

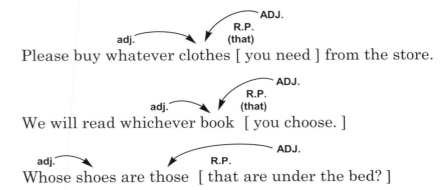

Please buy whatever clothes [you need] from the store.

We will read whichever book [you choose.]

Whose shoes are those [that are under the bed?]

Proceed to Worksheets 76 and 77.

NOTES

Directions for Worksheet 78

Worksheet 78 provides sentences containing adjective and adverb clauses; it also includes noun clauses functioning as direct objects and indirect objects.

Note: Review definition of indirect object.

Sentences for class presentation:

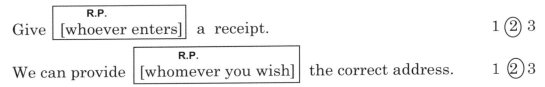

Give | **R.P.** [whoever enters] | a receipt.   1 ②3

We can provide | **R.P.** [whomever you wish] | the correct address.   1 ②3

Proceed to Worksheet 78.

Directions for Worksheet 79

Worksheet 79 includes sentences with adjective and adverb clauses; noun clauses acting as direct objects, indirect objects, and **predicate nominatives** are also included.

Note: Review definition of predicate nominative.

Sentences for class presentation:

                P.N.
      R.P.
This is [what she firmly believes.]   1 ②3

                P.N.
      R.P.
That was definitely [why I came here.]   1 ②3

Students should bracket only dependent clauses.

A cumulative quiz follows Worksheet 79.

Proceed to Worksheet 79.

Directions for Worksheet 80

Noun clauses that act as objects of prepositions are introduced on Worksheet 80.

Sentences for class presentation:

                          O.P.
                       R.P.
You may present this to [whomever you wish.]   1 ②3

                           O.P.
                 R.P.
They got there by [whatever means were available.] 1 ②3

                    O.P.
               R.P.
I disagree with [what you say.]   1 ②3

Proceed to Worksheet 80.

Directions for Worksheet 81

Worksheet 81 provides sentences containing noun clauses that act as appositives.

Note: **Review definition of appositive.**

Sentences for class presentation:

                       APP.
          R.P.
The winner, [whoever comes in with the largest fish,]

will receive a prize.   1 ②3

                  APP.
         R.P.
The new policy, [whatever we decide ,] will affect many people. 1 ②3

Proceed to Worksheet 81.

NOTES

33

Directions for Worksheet 82

Worksheet 82 includes noun clauses used as subjects. At this point, students should be able to bracket all dependent clauses accurately and rapidly.

Sentences for class presentation:

                S
      R.P.
    [What I see] isn't very pretty.   1 ② 3

                        S
      R.P.
    [Whoever broke this window] will be sorry.   1 ② 3

                  S
      R.P.
    [How this happened] is a mystery to me.   1 ② 3

Proceed to Worksheet 82.

Directions for Worksheets 83-85

Worksheets 83-85 provide sentences containing various dependent clauses. Students showing mastery are ready for the **Advanced Grammar Post Test**.

A general review of all topics covered should precede administration of the Post Test. Many teachers find that practicing the quizzes from the program is an effective method of review.

Proceed to Worksheets 83-85.

NOTES

WORKSHEET 31

Identify only the parts of speech indicated for each group of sentences.
Sentences 1-5. Put a check (√) over all articles, and underline all nouns.

*tricky sentences

1. Mary and I saw Elvis Presley in a√ movie at the√

    Argosy Theater on Wednesday.

2. The Oklahoma√ Sooners will play in the Orange√ Bowl on

    New Year's Eve.

*3. We came home Friday, but she wasn't there.

*4. European women enjoy American magazines.

5. We caught trout, bass and sunfish from the√ pier at the√

    lake.

Sentences 6-10. Write **pron.** over all personal pronouns.

6. We(pron.) will visit them(pron.) before the Christmas vacation.

7. She(pron.) gave it(pron.) to them(pron.) after she(pron.) finished it(pron.).

8. They(pron.) will tell us(pron.) about it(pron.).

*9. Tell(You)(pron.) us(pron.) a story and tuck us(pron.) in.

*10. Thank you(pron.), Ned, for the wonderful time we(pron.) had.

Notes: 3. **Home, Friday**, and **there** are adverbs answering when and where that modify the verbs.
   4. **European** and **American** are capitalized, but function as adjectives.
   9. **You** is an ellipsis and could be overlooked as a pronoun.
   10. **You** as part of **thank you** is a pronoun.

WORKSHEET 32

Double underline all verbs and helping verbs in sentences 1-10. Circle **A** if the main verb is an action verb. Circle **L** if the main verb is a linking verb.

*tricky sentences

1. The diner <u>closes</u> at 10:00 p.m., Don.   Ⓐ L

2. <u>Is</u> the spider deadly or harmless?   A Ⓛ

3. <u>Will</u> you <u>run</u> around the block?   Ⓐ L

4. <u>Have</u> you <u>spent</u> the money yet?   Ⓐ L

5. He <u>will</u> <u>become</u> wealthy in a few years.   A Ⓛ

6. <u>Sit</u> and <u>think</u> about it for a while.   1. Ⓐ L

                                                          2. Ⓐ L

*7. She'<u>s</u> afraid of the dark, Todd.   A Ⓛ

*8. The radio <u>won't</u> <u>be</u> <u>fixed</u> before tonight.   Ⓐ L

9. Chickens and turkeys <u>can't</u> <u>fly</u> away from the farm.   Ⓐ L

10. He'<u>ll</u> <u>be</u> back from the Army in mid-February.   A Ⓛ

Notes: 7. **Afraid** is an adjective.
        8. There are two helping verbs besides the action verb.

WORKSHEET 33

Write **adj.** over all adjectives, and write **adv.** over all adverbs. Draw arrows to the words they modify. Do not identify prepositional phrases.

*tricky sentences

1. The ugly monster attacked the beautiful princess.

2. He carefully turned the knob on the old safe.

*3. Doesn't Ted seem taller in the recent picture?

4. Dry weather always worries farmers.

*5. The birthday cake was very quickly eaten.

6. We camped Wednesday near the ghost town.

7. Soon you'll see the reason for the big decision.

*8. Up went the red and white balloon.

9. I am not very good with the yo-yo.

10. He rarely dines alone; he invites a neighbor or friend

along.

Notes: 3. Questions usually must be inverted to sentences to find the subject and verb. Taking out contractions helps the student see the adverb **not**. **Ted does not seem taller...**
5. The verb is **was eaten**; **very** and **quickly** are adverbs.
8. Students might get confused and not see that the subject is **balloon**. The sentence must be inverted to decode it easily.

WORKSHEET 34

Write **prep.** over all prepositions. Write **O.P.** over all objects of prepositions. Put all prepositional phrases in parentheses **( )**. Identify each phrase as an **ADJ.** or **ADV.** Draw an arrow to the word each phrase modifies.

*tricky sentences

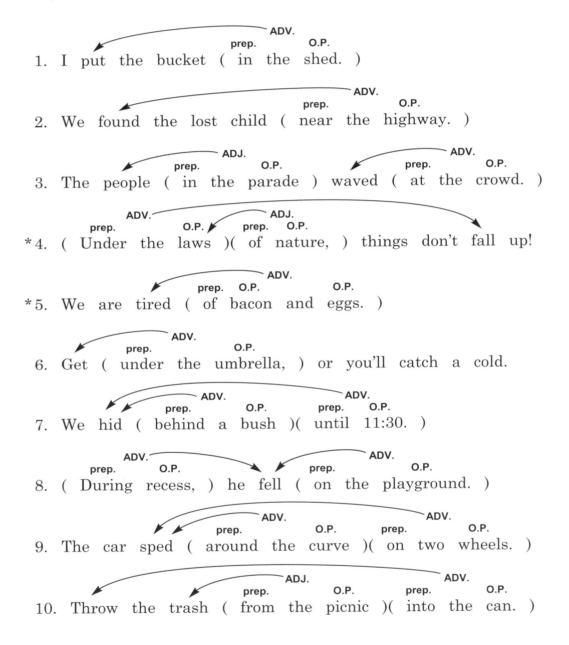

1. I put the bucket (in the shed.)

2. We found the lost child (near the highway.)

3. The people (in the parade) waved (at the crowd.)

*4. (Under the laws)(of nature,) things don't fall up!

*5. We are tired (of bacon and eggs.)

6. Get (under the umbrella,) or you'll catch a cold.

7. We hid (behind a bush)(until 11:30.)

8. (During recess,) he fell (on the playground.)

9. The car sped (around the curve)(on two wheels.)

10. Throw the trash (from the picnic)(into the can.)

Notes: 4. **Under the laws** tells where things fall; **of nature** answers which laws.
       5. There are two objects of the preposition.

38

WORKSHEET 35

Underline all nouns, double-underline all verbs, and write **c.c.** over all coordinating conjunctions in sentences 1-5.

*tricky sentences

1. We <u>were</u> hungry **c.c.** yet happy after the <u>hike</u>.

2. <u>Bill</u> and I **c.c.** <u>will</u> <u>build</u> and **c.c.** <u>furnish</u> the new <u>cabin</u>.

3. You <u>rake</u> the <u>leaves</u>, and **c.c.** I <u>will</u> <u>bag</u> them.

*4. Never <u>approach</u> an angry <u>dog</u> ; **c.c.** you <u>may</u> <u>be</u> sorry.

5. I've never <u>cheated</u> in <u>school</u>, nor **c.c.** <u>will</u> I!

Underline all nouns, double-underline all verbs, and put an exclamation mark over all interjections in sentences 6-10.

6. Wow **!** , <u>did</u> you <u>see</u> the <u>fireworks</u>?

*7. <u>Help</u>! We <u>can't</u> <u>find</u> the <u>way</u> out.

8. <u>Get</u> out of here, <u>mister</u>!

9. Oh **!** , you <u>don't</u> <u>mean</u> it!

10. Hey **!** ! I never <u>knew</u> you <u>had</u> a <u>brother</u>.

Notes: 4. Students may have forgotten that a **;** is a c.c.
7. Even though **Help!** has an exclamation mark by it, the word is actually the verb in the sentence **You help.**

WORKSHEET 36

Underline every noun in the following sentences. Write **pron.** over every personal pronoun. Using the noun function cards 1-8, mark the function for each noun and each pronoun.

EVERY NOUN AND EVERY PRONOUN IN A SENTENCE MUST PERFORM A NOUN FUNCTION!

*tricky sentences

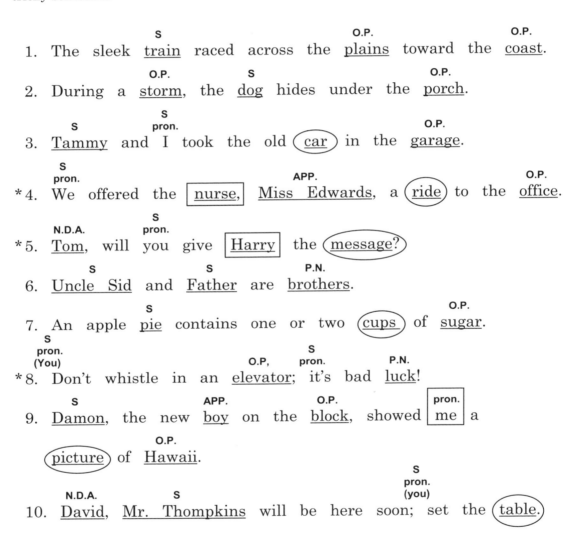

1. The sleek <u>train</u> raced across the <u>plains</u> toward the <u>coast</u>.

2. During a <u>storm</u>, the <u>dog</u> hides under the <u>porch</u>.

3. <u>Tammy</u> and I took the old car in the <u>garage</u>.

*4. We offered the nurse, <u>Miss Edwards</u>, a ride to the <u>office</u>.

*5. <u>Tom</u>, will you give Harry the message?

6. <u>Uncle Sid</u> and <u>Father</u> are <u>brothers</u>.

7. An apple <u>pie</u> contains one or two cups of <u>sugar</u>.

*8. Don't whistle in an <u>elevator</u>; it's bad <u>luck</u>!

9. <u>Damon</u>, the new <u>boy</u> on the <u>block</u>, showed me a picture of <u>Hawaii</u>.

10. <u>David</u>, <u>Mr. Thompkins</u> will be here soon; set the table.

Notes: 4. Students must see that a **ride** was offered and is the direct object. A ride was offered to the nurse.
5. **Tom** is not the subject of this sentence
8. The student needs to remember the ellipsed subject **you** is a pronoun.

40

WORKSHEET 37

Underline all nouns. Write **pron.** over every personal pronoun. Using the noun function cards, mark the function for each noun and each pronoun.
EVERY NOUN AND EVERY PRONOUN IN A SENTENCE MUST PERFORM A NOUN FUNCTION!

*tricky sentences

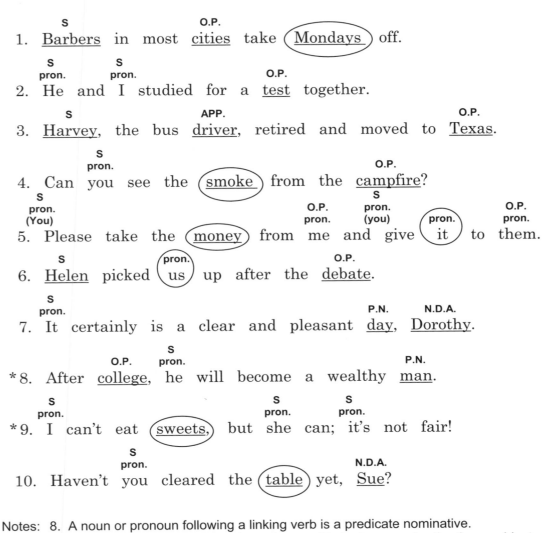

1. Barbers in most cities take Mondays off.

2. He and I studied for a test together.

3. Harvey, the bus driver, retired and moved to Texas.

4. Can you see the smoke from the campfire?

5. Please take the money from me and give it to them.

6. Helen picked us up after the debate.

7. It certainly is a clear and pleasant day, Dorothy.

*8. After college, he will become a wealthy man.

*9. I can't eat sweets, but she can; it's not fair!

10. Haven't you cleared the table yet, Sue?

Notes: 8. A noun or pronoun following a linking verb is a predicate nominative.
　　　　9. There are three clauses in this sentence. Students may miss the three subjects.

41

WORKSHEET 38

Underline all nouns. Write **pron.** over every personal pronoun. Using the noun function cards, mark the function for each noun and each pronoun.
  EVERY NOUN AND EVERY PRONOUN IN A SENTENCE MUST PERFORM A NOUN FUNCTION!

*tricky sentences

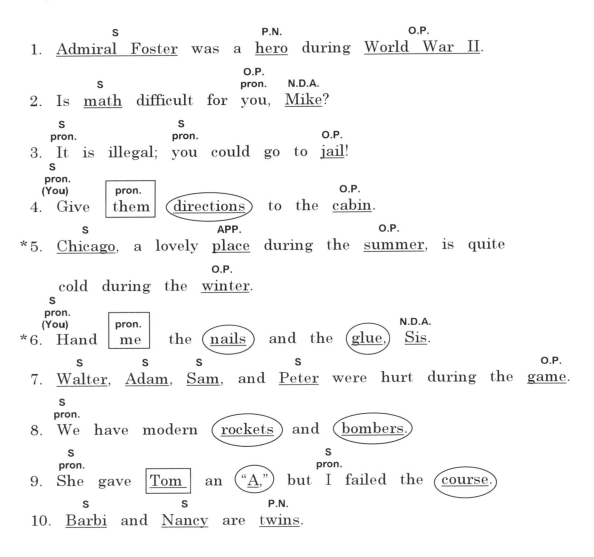

1. Admiral Foster was a hero during World War II.
   S — P.N. — O.P.

2. Is math difficult for you, Mike?
   S — O.P. pron. — N.D.A.

3. It is illegal; you could go to jail!
   S pron. — S pron. — O.P.

4. Give them directions to the cabin.
   S pron. (You) — pron. — O.P.

*5. Chicago, a lovely place during the summer, is quite cold during the winter.
   S — APP. — O.P. — O.P.

*6. Hand me the nails and the glue, Sis.
   S pron. (You) — pron. — N.D.A.

7. Walter, Adam, Sam, and Peter were hurt during the game.
   S — S — S — S — O.P.

8. We have modern rockets and bombers.
   S pron.

9. She gave Tom an "A," but I failed the course.
   S pron. — S — P.N.

10. Barbi and Nancy are twins.
    S — S — P.N.

Notes: 5. Students may miss the appositive in the word **place** since it has an adj. before it and a descriptive prepositional phrase following it.
      6. There is a compound direct object.

42

WORKSHEET 39

Underline all nouns. Write **pron.** over every personal pronoun. Using the noun function cards, mark the function for each noun and each pronoun.

EVERY NOUN AND EVERY PRONOUN IN A SENTENCE MUST PERFORM A NOUN FUNCTION!

*tricky sentences

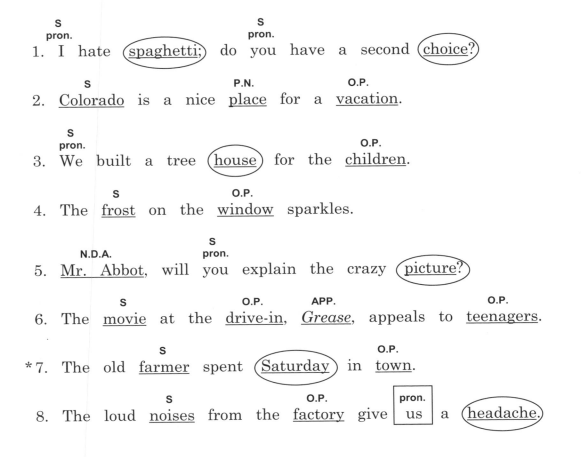

1. I hate spaghetti; do you have a second choice?

2. Colorado is a nice place for a vacation.

3. We built a tree house for the children.

4. The frost on the window sparkles.

5. Mr. Abbot, will you explain the crazy picture?

6. The movie at the drive-in, *Grease*, appeals to teenagers.

*7. The old farmer spent Saturday in town.

8. The loud noises from the factory give us a headache.

Notes: 7. Even though **Saturday** may act as an adverb in many cases, here it functions as a noun. The farmer spent what in town? Saturday.

WORKSHEET 40

Underline all nouns. Write **pron.** over every personal pronoun. Using the noun function cards, mark the function for each noun and each pronoun.

  EVERY NOUN AND EVERY PRONOUN IN A SENTENCE MUST PERFORM A NOUN FUNCTION!

*tricky sentences

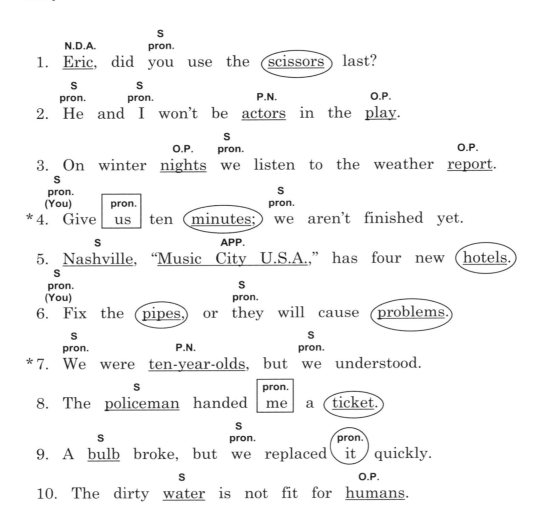

1. Eric, did you use the scissors last?
   N.D.A.   S/pron.   S

2. He and I won't be actors in the play.
   S/pron. S/pron.   P.N.   O.P.

3. On winter nights we listen to the weather report.
              O.P. S/pron.   O.P.

*4. Give us ten minutes; we aren't finished yet.
   S/pron. pron.   S   S/pron.
   (You)

5. Nashville, "Music City U.S.A.," has four new hotels.
   S   APP.

6. Fix the pipes, or they will cause problems.
   S/pron. S   S/pron.   S
   (You)

*7. We were ten-year-olds, but we understood.
    S/pron.   P.N.   S/pron.

8. The policeman handed me a ticket.
        S   pron.   S

9. A bulb broke, but we replaced it quickly.
        S   S/pron. pron.

10. The dirty water is not fit for humans.
              S   O.P.

Notes: 4. Students might mistake the indirect object **us** for the ellipsed subject **You.**
       7. Hyphenated word phrases are treated as one word.

44

WORKSHEET 41

Worksheet 41 involves possessive adjectives. Your new orange card with the blue border lists these words. Mark all nouns and pronouns and indicate noun functions. Write **adj.** over all adjectives, and draw arrows to the words they modify. Use your cards. Do not identify prepositional phrases.

*tricky sentences

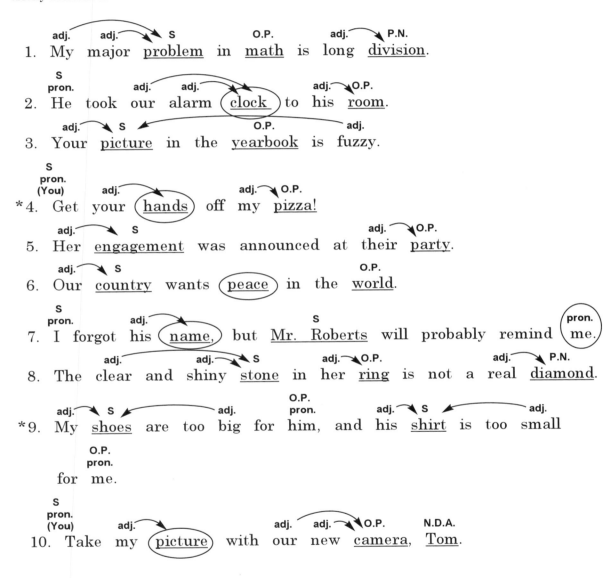

1. My major problem in math is long division.

2. He took our alarm clock to his room.

3. Your picture in the yearbook is fuzzy.

*4. Get your hands off my pizza!

5. Her engagement was announced at their party.

6. Our country wants peace in the world.

7. I forgot his name, but Mr. Roberts will probably remind me.

8. The clear and shiny stone in her ring is not a real diamond.

*9. My shoes are too big for him, and his shirt is too small for me.

10. Take my picture with our new camera, Tom.

Notes: 4. **Off** is used as a preposition.
        9. Both **big** and **small** are used as predicate adjectives.

45

WORKSHEET 42

You have been given a possessive pronoun card. Possessive pronouns always perform noun functions. Note that **his** is sometimes an adjective. Be careful when you see **his**. If it performs a noun function, it is a pronoun. Identify all nouns and pronouns; mark their functions.

*tricky sentences

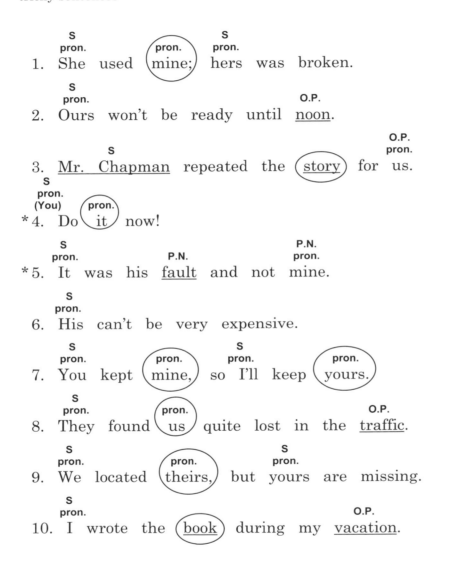

1. She used mine; hers was broken.

2. Ours won't be ready until noon.

3. Mr. Chapman repeated the story for us.

*4. Do it now!

*5. It was his fault and not mine.

6. His can't be very expensive.

7. You kept mine, so I'll keep yours.

8. They found us quite lost in the traffic.

9. We located theirs, but yours are missing.

10. I wrote the book during my vacation.

Notes: 4. Students may mistake **it** for the subject instead of the ellipsed **You**.
     5. This sentence contains a compound predicate nominative.

46

WORKSHEET 43

Underline all nouns and mark all pronouns. Indicate the noun function each noun and pronoun performs. Mark all adjectives and draw arrows to the words they modify.

*tricky sentences

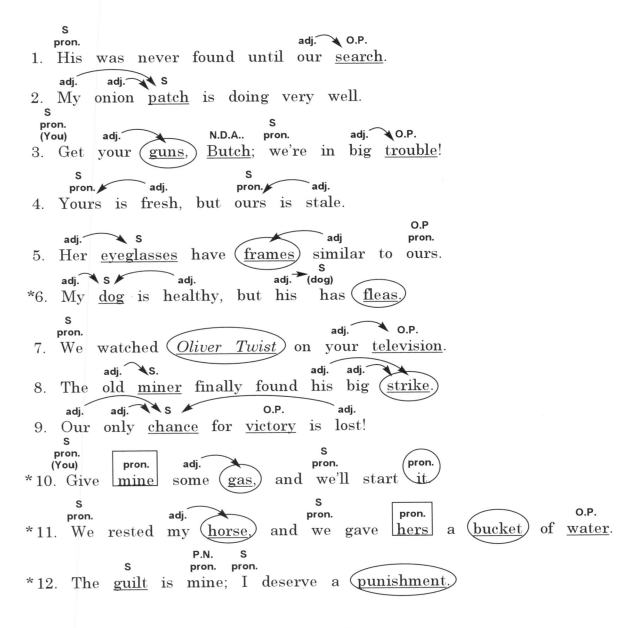

1. His was never found until our search.

2. My onion patch is doing very well.

3. Get your (guns,) Butch; we're in big trouble!

4. Yours is fresh, but ours is stale.

5. Her eyeglasses have (frames) similar to ours.

*6. My dog is healthy, but his has (fleas.)

7. We watched (Oliver Twist) on your television.

8. The old miner finally found his big (strike.)

9. Our only chance for victory is lost!

*10. Give mine some (gas,) and we'll start it.

*11. We rested my (horse,) and we gave hers a (bucket) of water.

*12. The guilt is mine; I deserve a (punishment.)

Notes: 6. Alternately, **his** could be a pronoun and be the subject.
10. **Mine** comes between the action and the direct object; so it is an indirect object
11. **Hers** comes between the action and the direct object. **Hers** is a pronoun and never an adjective.
12. **Mine** comes after a linking verb and renames the subject, so it is a P.N.

47

WORKSHEET 44

This worksheet contains many possessives. Underline all nouns. Mark all pronouns with **pron.** Indicate all noun functions. Write **adj.** above adjectives and draw arrows to the words they modify.

*tricky sentences

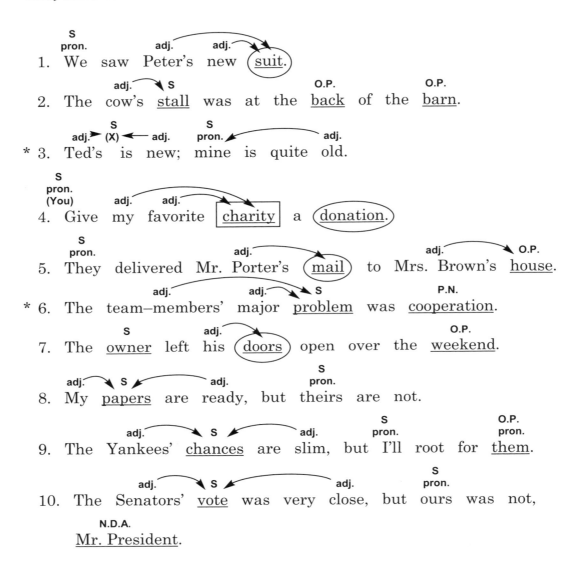

1. We   saw   Peter's   new   (suit.)

2. The   cow's   stall   was   at   the   back   of   the   barn.

* 3. Ted's   is   new;   mine   is   quite   old.

4. Give   my   favorite   [charity]   a   (donation.)

5. They   delivered   Mr. Porter's   (mail)   to   Mrs. Brown's   house.

* 6. The   team–members'   major   problem   was   cooperation.

7. The   owner   left   his   (doors)   open   over   the   weekend.

8. My   papers   are   ready,   but   theirs   are   not.

9. The   Yankees'   chances   are   slim,   but   I'll   root   for   them.

10. The   Senators'   vote   was   very   close,   but   ours   was   not,

Mr. President.

Notes: 3. Because Ted has an **'s** on the end, it must function as a possessive adj. If the subject is not known, an **X** is used to signify the noun function.
6. **Team-members** is treated as one word.

WORKSHEET 45

Underline all <u>nouns</u>. Write **pron.** over all pronouns. Indicate noun functions. Write **adj.** over all adjectives and draw a line to words modified. These are <u>all</u> tricky!

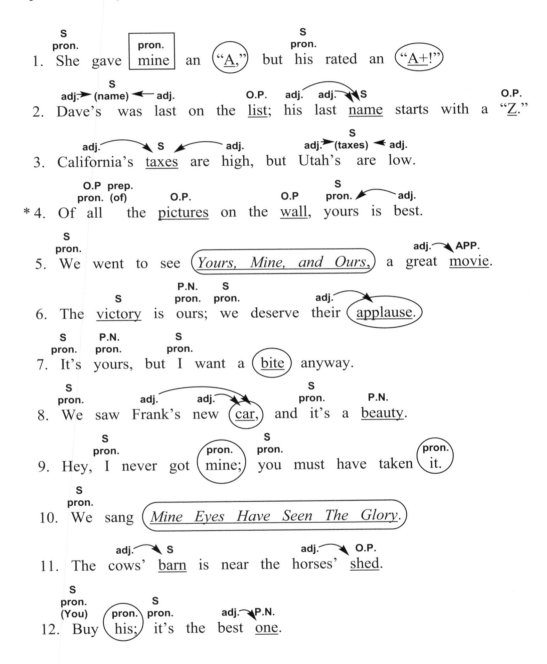

1. She gave mine an "A," but his rated an "A+!"

2. Dave's was last on the <u>list</u>; his last <u>name</u> starts with a "<u>Z</u>."

3. California's <u>taxes</u> are high, but Utah's are low.

*4. Of all the <u>pictures</u> on the <u>wall</u>, yours is best.

5. We went to see *Yours, Mine, and Ours,* a great <u>movie</u>.

6. The <u>victory</u> is ours; we deserve their <u>applause</u>.

7. It's yours, but I want a bite anyway.

8. We saw Frank's new car, and it's a <u>beauty</u>.

9. Hey, I never got mine; you must have taken it.

10. We sang *Mine Eyes Have Seen The Glory*.

11. The cows' <u>barn</u> is near the horses' <u>shed</u>.

12. Buy his; it's the best <u>one</u>.

Note: 4. This sentence is especially hard as the preposition is ellipsed.

49

WORKSHEET 46

The following words are often either adjectives or pronouns. **They are pronouns if they perform noun functions in a sentence.** They are adjectives if they modify nouns.

this	that	these	those	which
whose	what	all	any	another
anyone	both	each	either	everybody
nobody	none	one, two, three….		something
other	several	somebody	some	someone

In the sentences below, underline all nouns, write **pron.** over all pronouns, and mark all adjectives **adj.** Mark all nouns and pronouns for noun function. Draw arrows from adjectives to the words they modify.

1. Few people want their children in that school.
   - adj. → S (people)
   - adj. → (children) S
   - adj. → school O.P.

2. Several plants died in the sun, but some didn't.
   - adj. → S (plants)
   - sun O.P.
   - some S pron.

3. Three of us will go with them.
   - S pron. (Three)
   - O.P. pron. (us)
   - O.P. pron. (them)

4. Many foreign countries trade with the U.S.A.
   - adj. adj. → S (countries)
   - U.S.A. O.P.

5. I took two, and she took five.
   - S pron. (I)
   - pron. (two)
   - S pron. (she)
   - pron. (five)

6. Nobody came to the door of their apartment.
   - S pron. (Nobody)
   - door O.P.
   - adj. → apartment O.P.

7. She gave most of her wealth to charity.
   - S pron. (She)
   - pron. (most)
   - adj. → wealth O.P.
   - charity O.P.

8. You may have either one, Tom.
   - S pron. (You)
   - adj. → one pron.
   - Tom N.D.A.

WORKSHEET 47

Underline all nouns. Write **pron.** over all pronouns. Mark all noun functions.
Identify adjectives with **adj.**, and draw arrows to the words they modify.

*tricky sentences

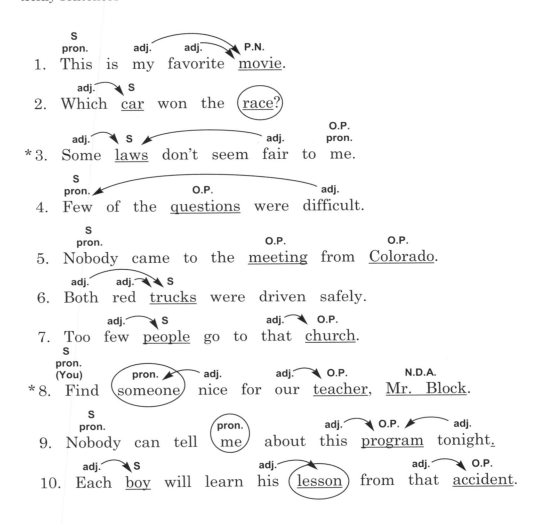

1. This is my favorite movie.

2. Which car won the race?

*3. Some laws don't seem fair to me.

4. Few of the questions were difficult.

5. Nobody came to the meeting from Colorado.

6. Both red trucks were driven safely.

7. Too few people go to that church.

*8. Find someone nice for our teacher, Mr. Block.

9. Nobody can tell me about this program tonight.

10. Each boy will learn his lesson from that accident.

Notes: 3. **Some** does not function as an pronoun here, but describes **laws**.
8. **Mr. Block** cannot be an appositive here as he is the one being addressed.

51

WORKSHEET 48

Underline all nouns. Write **pron.** over all pronouns. Mark all noun functions. Identify adjectives with **adj.**, and draw arrows to the words they modify.

*tricky sentences

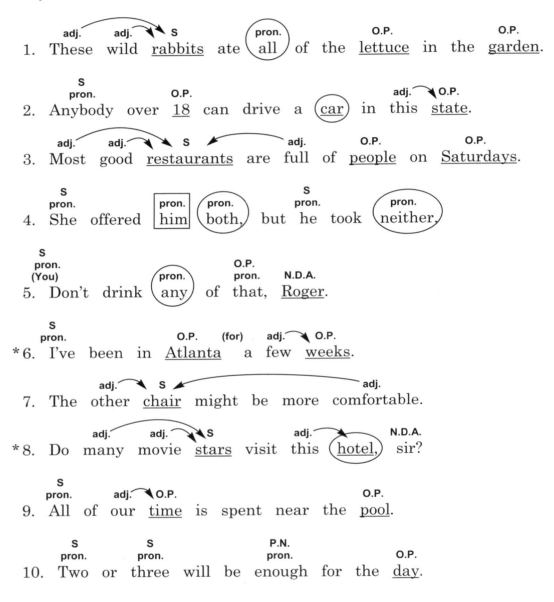

1. These wild rabbits ate all of the lettuce in the garden.

2. Anybody over 18 can drive a car in this state.

3. Most good restaurants are full of people on Saturdays.

4. She offered him both, but he took neither.

5. Don't drink any of that, Roger.

*6. I've been in Atlanta a few weeks.

7. The other chair might be more comfortable.

*8. Do many movie stars visit this hotel, sir?

9. All of our time is spent near the pool.

10. Two or three will be enough for the day.

Notes: 6. The ellipsed preposition **for** makes this sentence difficult.
   8. **Movie** is usually thought of as a noun, but here functions as an adjective.

WORKSHEET 49

Words ending in **–self** or **–selves** are pronouns. If they perform a noun function, indicate their use in the sentence. Mark <u>all</u> pronouns with **pron.** and indicate their functions (if any).

*tricky sentences

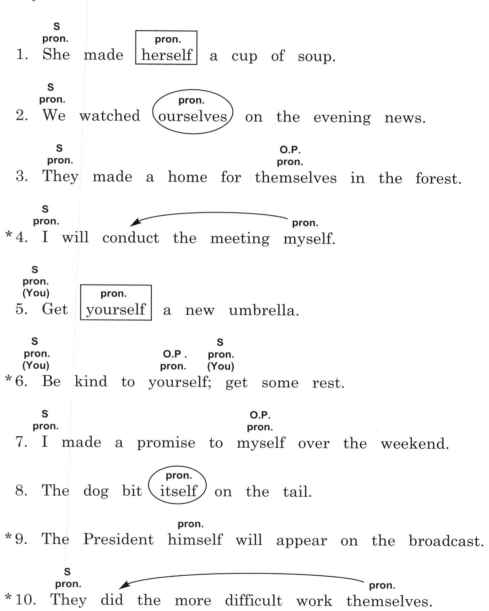

1. She made herself a cup of soup.

2. We watched ourselves on the evening news.

3. They made a home for themselves in the forest.

*4. I will conduct the meeting myself.

5. Get yourself a new umbrella.

*6. Be kind to yourself; get some rest.

7. I made a promise to myself over the weekend.

8. The dog bit itself on the tail.

*9. The President himself will appear on the broadcast.

*10. They did the more difficult work themselves.

Notes: 4 and 10. **Themselves** is used as an adverb.
  6. Both clauses have ellipsed subjects.
  9. **Himself** is used as an intensifier.

53

WORKSHEET 50

Who, whom, which, what, whose often introduce questions. If they perform noun functions, they are pronouns. If they modify nouns, they are adjectives.
Identify all nouns and pronouns in the following sentences. Mark all noun functions. ON A SEPARATE SHEET, REARRANGE QUESTIONS AS STATEMENTS IF NECESSARY.

Example: Who will be our teacher?

Our teacher will be who?

*tricky sentences

1. Whose can we borrow today?

2. Which can move fastest?

*3. What decision have you reached?

4. What will the answer be, Ted?

5. Who will clean the den after the party?

6. Whom can I ask about the garage sale?

7. Which team will wear white jerseys?

*8. Whose paint spilled on the new carpet?

Notes: 3. Who is doing the action? **You have reached**…
8. **Whose** is used as an adjective in this case.

54

WORKSHEET 51

Mark all nouns, pronouns, and adjectives. Identify all noun functions. Rearrange questions as statements if necessary.

*tricky sentences

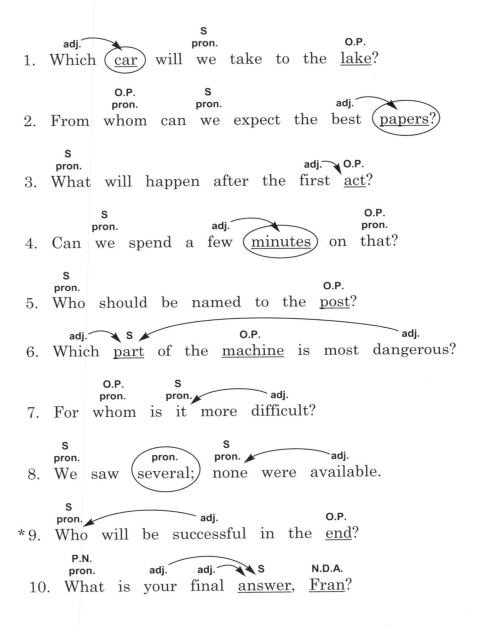

1. Which car will we take to the lake?

2. From whom can we expect the best papers?

3. What will happen after the first act?

4. Can we spend a few minutes on that?

5. Who should be named to the post?

6. Which part of the machine is most dangerous?

7. For whom is it more difficult?

8. We saw several; none were available.

*9. Who will be successful in the end?

10. What is your final answer, Fran?

Note: 9. While many questions must be inverted, this one does not.

WORKSHEET 52

The words **where, why, when**, and **how** often introduce simple questions. When they do, they are adverbs. Change questions to statements if necessary, and mark all adverbs, adjectives, nouns, and pronouns. Identify all noun functions. Draw arrows from adverbs and adjectives to the words they modify.

*tricky sentences

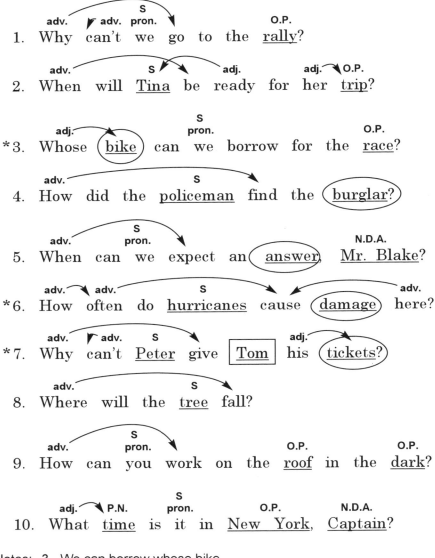

1. Why can't we go to the rally?

2. When will Tina be ready for her trip?

*3. Whose bike can we borrow for the race?

4. How did the policeman find the burglar?

5. When can we expect an answer, Mr. Blake?

*6. How often do hurricanes cause damage here?

*7. Why can't Peter give Tom his tickets?

8. Where will the tree fall?

9. How can you work on the roof in the dark?

10. What time is it in New York, Captain?

Notes: 3. We can borrow whose bike...
        6. Hurricanes do cause damage here how often.
        7. Peter can not give Tom...
        10. It is what time...

56

WORKSHEET 53

Identify all nouns, pronouns, verbs and adjectives. Draw arrows from adjectives to the words they modify. Mark all noun functions. Watch out for words ending in **-ing**.

*tricky sentences

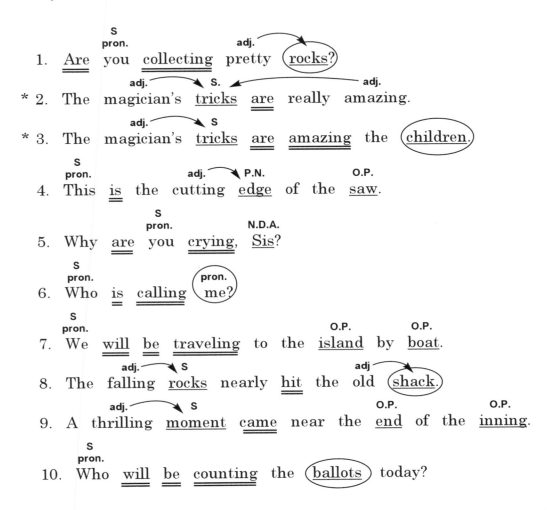

1. Are you collecting pretty rocks?

* 2. The magician's tricks are really amazing.

* 3. The magician's tricks are amazing the children.

4. This is the cutting edge of the saw.

5. Why are you crying, Sis?

6. Who is calling me?

7. We will be traveling to the island by boat.

8. The falling rocks nearly hit the old shack.

9. A thrilling moment came near the end of the inning.

10. Who will be counting the ballots today?

Notes: 2 and 3. Amazing is used as describing the tricks where in sentence 3 amazing is used as an action verb.

WORKSHEET 54

Identify all nouns, pronouns, verbs and adjectives. Draw arrows from adjectives to the words they modify. Mark all noun functions. Watch out for words ending in **-ing**.

*tricky sentences

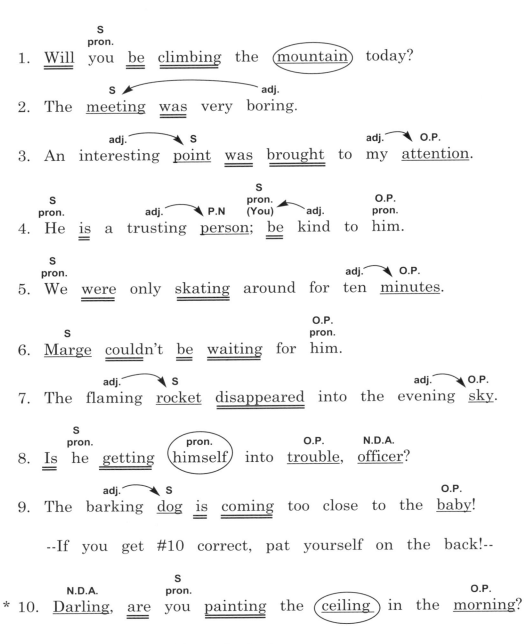

1. Will you be climbing the (mountain) today?

2. The meeting was very boring.

3. An interesting point was brought to my attention.

4. He is a trusting person; be kind to him.

5. We were only skating around for ten minutes.

6. Marge couldn't be waiting for him.

7. The flaming rocket disappeared into the evening sky.

8. Is he getting (himself) into trouble, officer?

9. The barking dog is coming too close to the baby!

--If you get #10 correct, pat yourself on the back!--

* 10. Darling, are you painting the (ceiling) in the morning?

Note: 10. Darling is an appositive ending in **-ing**.

58

WORKSHEET 55

Identify all nouns, pronouns, verbs and adjectives. Draw arrows from adjectives to the words they modify. Mark all noun functions. Watch out for words ending in **-ing**.

*tricky sentences

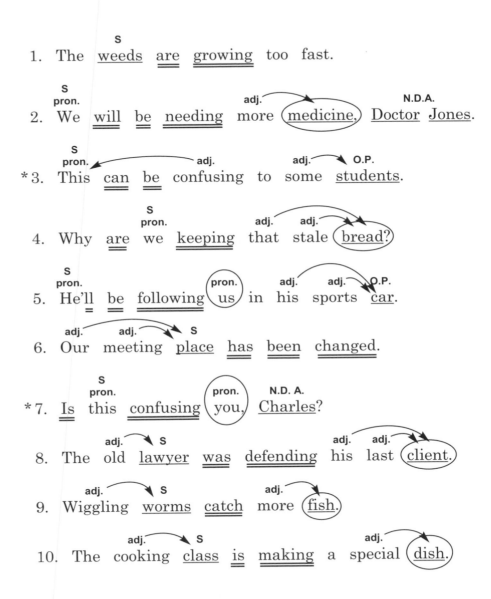

1. The <u>weeds</u> <u>are</u> <u>growing</u> too fast.

2. We <u>will</u> <u>be</u> <u>needing</u> more (medicine,) Doctor Jones.

*3. This <u>can</u> <u>be</u> confusing to some <u>students</u>.

4. Why <u>are</u> we <u>keeping</u> that stale (bread?)

5. He'll be <u>following</u> (us) in his sports <u>car</u>.

6. Our meeting <u>place</u> <u>has</u> <u>been</u> <u>changed</u>.

*7. <u>Is</u> this <u>confusing</u> (you,) <u>Charles</u>?

8. The old <u>lawyer</u> <u>was</u> <u>defending</u> his last (client.)

9. Wiggling <u>worms</u> <u>catch</u> more (fish.)

10. The cooking <u>class</u> <u>is</u> <u>making</u> a special (dish.)

Notes: 3. **Confusing** describes a state whereas in sentence 7 **confusing** is the action verb.

WORKSHEET 56

Identify all nouns, pronouns, and adjectives; mark noun functions and draw arrows.
*tricky sentences

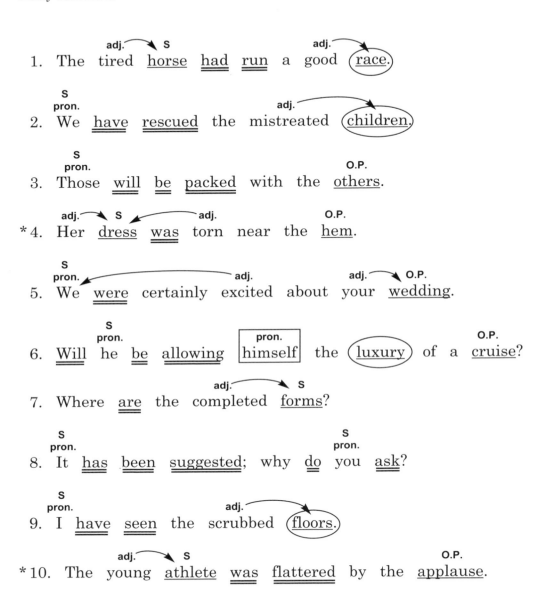

1. The tired horse had run a good race.

2. We have rescued the mistreated children.

3. Those will be packed with the others.

*4. Her dress was torn near the hem.

5. We were certainly excited about your wedding.

6. Will he be allowing himself the luxury of a cruise?

7. Where are the completed forms?

8. It has been suggested; why do you ask?

9. I have seen the scrubbed floors.

*10. The young athlete was flattered by the applause.

Notes: 4. Alternatively, the student could correctly mark **was torn** as a verb phrase.
       10. **Was flattered** is a passive verb as in the sentence 'The tree was trimmed by the man.'

WORKSHEET 57

Mark all nouns, pronouns, verbs and adjectives. Identify all noun functions. Draw arrows to words modified.

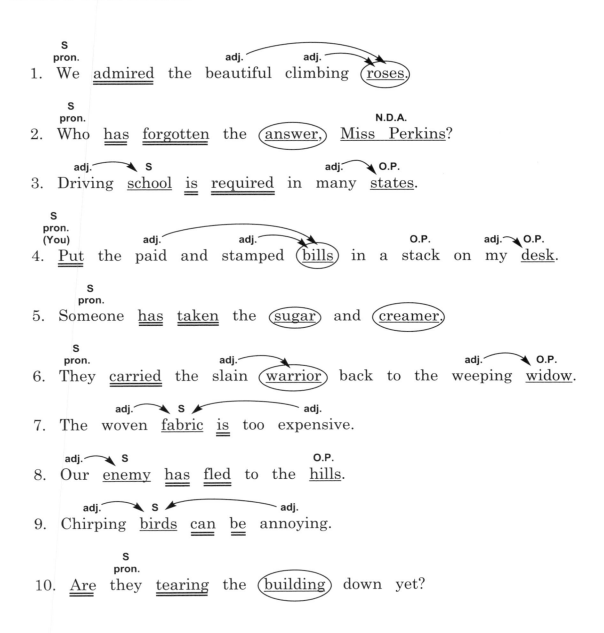

1. We admired the beautiful climbing roses.

2. Who has forgotten the answer, Miss Perkins?

3. Driving school is required in many states.

4. Put the paid and stamped bills in a stack on my desk.

5. Someone has taken the sugar and creamer.

6. They carried the slain warrior back to the weeping widow.

7. The woven fabric is too expensive.

8. Our enemy has fled to the hills.

9. Chirping birds can be annoying.

10. Are they tearing the building down yet?

WORKSHEET 58

Mark all nouns, pronouns, and verbs in the following sentences. Identify all noun functions. Mark all conjunctions with **c.c.**

Coordinating Conjunctions: **and but for yet or nor ;**

Correlative Conjunctions:

both....and	**not only....but also**
either...or	**neither......nor**

*tricky sentences

1. Either the rain will stop, or we'll cancel the picnic.

*2. Not only am I graduating, but I am also at the top of my class.

3. Either leave or start your work, Bill.

4. We received both a lecture and a punishment.

5. I want neither the salad nor the dessert.

6. The jungle cat is not only dangerous, but he is also smart.

*7. Both are trying, but neither will succeed.

8. Either I get my way, or I'll stop the game.

Notes: 3 and 6. **Not only ...but also** are more difficult as other words often come between them.

7. **Both** functions as a subject in this sentence, not a c.c.

WORKSHEET 59

Mark all simple infinitives with parentheses. Indicate their parts of speech. If the infinitive is a noun, mark its function. If the infinitive is an adjective or adverb, draw an arrow from the infinitive to the word modified.

*tricky sentences

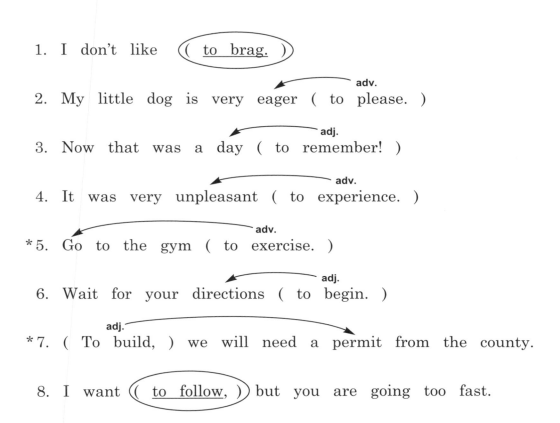

1. I don't like (to brag.)

2. My little dog is very eager (to please.)   adv.

3. Now that was a day (to remember!)   adj.

4. It was very unpleasant (to experience.)   adv.

*5. Go to the gym (to exercise.)   adv.

6. Wait for your directions (to begin.)   adj.

*7. adj. (To build,) we will need a permit from the county.

8. I want (to follow,) but you are going too fast.

Notes: 5. **The gym** is a noun, so **to the gym** is a prep phrase not an infinitive.
7. The meaning is not …need to build, but …permit to build.

63

WORKSHEET 60

Mark all simple infinitives with parentheses. Indicate their parts of speech. If the infinitive is a noun, mark its function. If the infinitive is an adjective or adverb, draw an arrow from the infinitive to the word modified.

*tricky sentences

1. We certainly need ((to leave,)) Johnny.

2. Scouts returned to the fort (to report.) **adv.**

3. The baby started ((to cry.))

*4. **adv.** (To succeed,) we must start a new business.

5. It is difficult (to understand.) **adv.**

6. **adv.** (To remember,) I tie a string on my finger.

7. Start ((to read;)) you only have another ten minutes.

*8. Get to bed and try ((to sleep.))

Notes: 4. **To succeed** can be moved to another part of this sentence without changing the meaning, so it is an adverb.
  8. **Bed** is a noun, so it is an O.P. **Sleep** here is used as a verb so **to sleep** is an infinitive.

WORKSHEET 61

Underline all nouns and write **pron.** above all pronouns. Identify all noun functions.
Gerunds are verb forms ending in **-ing** which perform noun functions. Underline all
gerunds and identify their noun functions.

Example:
                     S   P.N.
Stealing is a serious crime.
(Stealing is a gerund.)

      S   S
    pron.   pron.
1. We tried (skating,) but it was too difficult.

     S
   pron.   O.P.
2. He went out for wrestling.

              S   pron.   O.P.
3. The dentist charges me ($10) for a filling.

               S   O.P.
4. The old man smokes (cigars) after eating.

    S
  pron.
5. I could hear the (singing.)

        S   P.N.   O.P.
6. Voting is a citizen's duty in America.

        S   O.P.   O.P.
7. The children reached the (bottom) of the hill by sliding

            O.P.
on snow saucers.

         O.P.   S
8. Before relaxing, the mowing should be done.

WORKSHEET 62

Underline all nouns and write **pron.** above all pronouns. Identify all noun functions. Underline all gerunds and identify their noun functions. Remember: Gerunds are verb forms ending in **-ing** which perform noun functions.

Example:
                      S   P.N.
           Stealing is a serious crime.
           (Stealing is a gerund.)

*tricky sentences

         S   O.P.
1. Fighting is not allowed on the playground.

       S
      pron
2. We saw the (shooting) yesterday.

       S
      pron.
*3. I find (cooking) very difficult.

                      O.P.   S
*4. Watching from the window, the old lady was amused

                   O.P.
   by the giggling children.

         S
        pron.   O.P.   N.D.A.
5. Are you paying your (bills) on time, Barbara?

       S
      pron.   O.P.
6. We got a light (sprinkling) of rain today.

   S   O.P.   O.P.
7. Lying is forbidden in a court of law.

          S   P.N.
*8. Clam digging can be hard work.

         S   P.N.
9. Hunting dogs are often good house pets.

       S
      pron.   O.P.   O.P.
10. We drove in the country before returning.

Notes: 3. **Cooking**, although it is next to the verb, functions here as a thing, so is a noun.
       4. **Watching** is a present participle, an adjective modifying **lady**.
       8. **Clam** describes digging so is an adjective.

66

WORKSHEET 63

Mark all subjects and verbs. Circle the number of subject-verb combinations to each sentence below.

Example: **S**
  She <u>likes</u> chocolate. ① 2 3

*tricky sentences

  S
1. Bill <u>will</u> <u>lock</u> the door. ① 2 3

  S
2. We <u>have</u> a problem. ① 2 3

  S
3. We <u>promised</u> to be there. ① 2 3

  S
4. Circles <u>were</u> <u>drawn</u> on the page. ① 2 3

  S   **S**
5. Their plans and hopes <u>were</u> <u>realized</u>. ① 2 3

           S   **S**
                                            (you)
*6. Arguing <u>will</u> <u>get</u> you nowhere; <u>give</u> up. 1 ② 3

  S   **S**
7. She and I <u>waited</u> and <u>rested</u>. ① 2 3

  S
  (You)   **S**
8. <u>Provide</u> us with food, or we'<u>ll</u> <u>go</u> away. 1 ② 3

  S
  (You)   **S**
9. <u>Set</u> the clock for 6:00; I <u>need</u> to get up. 1 ② 3

  S
*10. She <u>tried</u> but <u>failed</u> to get her diploma. ① 2 3

Notes: 6. **Nowhere** is not a verb, so **you nowhere** is not a clause but a direct object and an adverb.
        10. **But failed** is not a clause as it has no subject. This is a compound verb in one clause.
        To get is an infinitive modifying the verbs.

WORKSHEET 64

Mark all subjects and verbs. Circle the number of subject-verb combinations to each sentence below.

Example: **S**   **S**

Walter <u>caught</u> a cold, but Sara <u>didn't</u>.   1 ②3 4

*tricky sentences

         S
        (You)
1. <u>Pick</u>   the beans near the fence first.   ①2 3 4

                S
               (you)
2. George, please <u>sit</u> behind the desk.   ①2 3 4

        S
*3. We <u>explored</u> caves, <u>climbed</u>   mountains,

       and <u>hiked</u> trails.   ①2 3 4

           S   **S**
4. Donald <u>can't</u> <u>decide</u> if he <u>wants</u> to go.   1 ②3 4

          S
5. Going to town <u>is</u> a big event.   ①2 3 4

     S   **S**
6. I <u>want</u> to see New York before I <u>leave</u>.   1 ②3 4

    S   **S**
   (You)   (you)
7. <u>Fill</u> the canteen, but <u>don't</u> <u>drink</u> any of the water. 1 ②3 4

     S   **S**
8. You <u>must</u> <u>be</u> mad; that <u>could</u> <u>be</u> dangerous!   1 ②3 4

     S   **S**
9. Jane <u>made</u> supper while Abe <u>cleaned</u> the den.   1 ②3 4

        S   **S**   **S**
10. The dog <u>barks</u>; the cat <u>howls</u>; the birds <u>chirp</u>;

      S
     I <u>can't</u> <u>get</u> any peace!   1 2 3 ④

Note: 3. While there are three verbs, there is only one subject, making this a single clause with a compound verb.

68

WORKSHEET 65

Count subject-verb combinations in the following sentences, and put brackets [ ] around each clause.

Example: S   S
                    [When we <u>win</u>,] [we <u>celebrate</u>.]   1 ②3

*tricky sentences

                S   S
1. [The robins <u>chirped</u>] [as we <u>approached</u>

the nest.]   1 ②3

                S   S
2. [The teacher <u>took</u> over] [while the principal

<u>was</u> away.]   1 ②3

            S   S
3. [Jim <u>can't</u> <u>do</u> the job] [because he <u>is</u> ill.]   1 ②3

                    S   S
4. [Until the votes <u>were</u> <u>counted</u>,] [we <u>were</u> nervous.] 1 ②3

        S
      (You)   S
*5. [<u>Get</u> the water] [while I <u>set</u> the table.]   1 ②3

                    S   S
6. [If the money <u>arrives</u>,] [we <u>will</u> <u>be</u> able to go.] 1 ②3

            S
7. [Painting with these brushes <u>is</u> impossible.]   ①2 3

                S   S
8. [The puppies and kittens <u>don't</u> <u>get</u> along.]   ①2 3

Note: 5. **(You) get...** and **I set...** -- two clauses in this sentence.

69

WORKSHEET 66

Count subject-verb combinations in the following sentences, and put brackets [ ]
around each clause.

Example: S S
[When we win,] [we celebrate.] 1 ② 3

*tricky sentences

1. [I am not listening to you, Tom.] ① 2 3

2. [Although he attended college,] [he didn't
   find work.] 1 ② 3

3. [Bill, wait] [until the rest of us finish.] 1 ② 3
   (you)

4. [Happy days followed their arrival in Paris.] ① 2 3

5. [May I talk with Sandy] [while you sleep?] 1 ② 3

6. [Vacuum the rug] [before you make the bed.] 1 ② 3
   (You)

7. [I left] [because I was tired.] 1 ② 3

8. [After the rain stopped,] [the game resumed.] 1 ② 3

*9. [After showering, he read the paper by the pool.] ① 2 3

10. [Though I disagree,] [you may have a point.] 1 ② 3

Note: 9. **Showering** is an O.P.

70

WORKSHEET 67

In the following sentences, mark and count subject-verb combinations, bracket clauses, and mark dependent clauses. Draw arrows from clauses to the words they modify. Label subordinating conjunctions **S.C.**

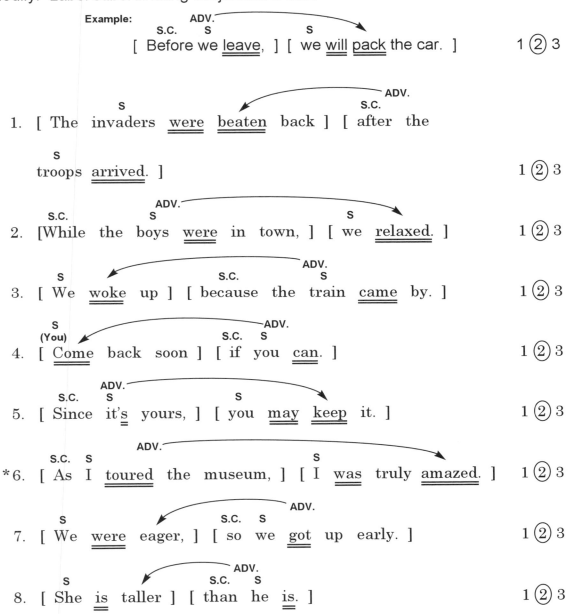

Example:

[Before we leave,] [we will pack the car.] 1 ② 3

1. [The invaders were beaten back] [after the troops arrived.] 1 ② 3

2. [While the boys were in town,] [we relaxed.] 1 ② 3

3. [We woke up] [because the train came by.] 1 ② 3

4. [Come back soon] [if you can.] 1 ② 3

5. [Since it's yours,] [you may keep it.] 1 ② 3

*6. [As I toured the museum,] [I was truly amazed.] 1 ② 3

7. [We were eager,] [so we got up early.] 1 ② 3

8. [She is taller] [than he is.] 1 ② 3

Note: 6. **Was amazed** is a passive verb as in 'I was laughing.'

WORKSHEET 68

In the following sentences, mark and count subject-verb combinations, bracket clauses, and mark dependent clauses. Draw arrows from clauses to the words they modify. Label subordinating conjunctions.

*tricky sentences

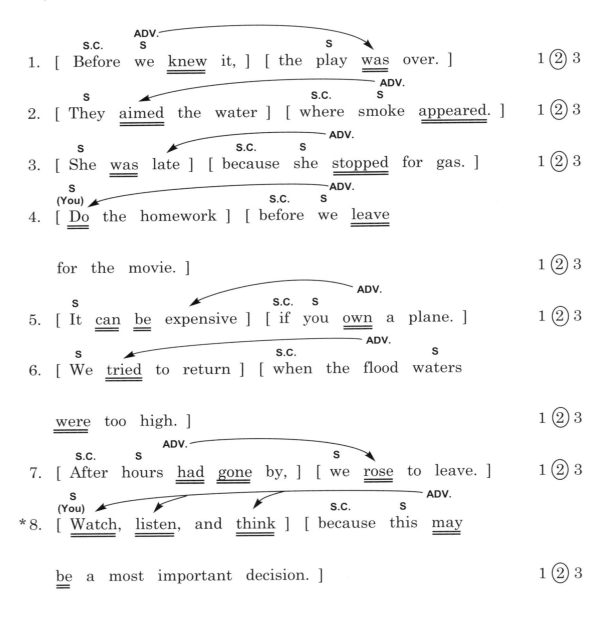

1. [Before we knew it,] [the play was over.]   1 ② 3

2. [They aimed the water] [where smoke appeared.]   1 ② 3

3. [She was late] [because she stopped for gas.]   1 ② 3

4. [Do the homework] [before we leave

   for the movie.]   1 ② 3

5. [It can be expensive] [if you own a plane.]   1 ② 3

6. [We tried to return] [when the flood waters

   were too high.]   1 ② 3

7. [After hours had gone by,] [we rose to leave.]   1 ② 3

*8. [Watch, listen, and think] [because this may

   be a most important decision.]   1 ② 3

Note: 8. The independent clause has a compound verb; the dependent clause modifies each verb in the independent clause.

72

WORKSHEET 69

Count subject-verb combinations. Bracket all clauses. Identify subordinating conjunctions (S.C.) and draw arrows from adverb clauses to the words they modify.

Examples:

A. [The beach was fine,] but [the lake was rough.]   1 ②3

B. [You try to read] [while we are waiting,]

   or [you'll be wasting time .]   1 2 ③

*tricky sentences

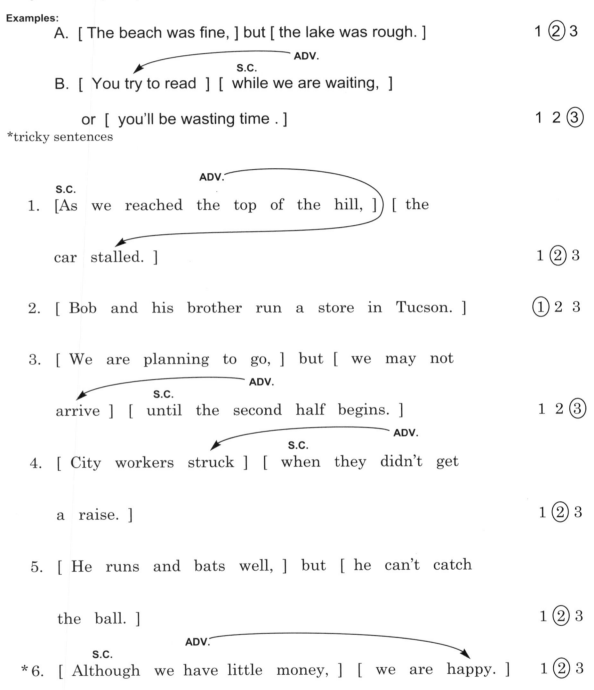

1. [As we reached the top of the hill,] [the

   car stalled.]   1 ②3

2. [Bob and his brother run a store in Tucson.]   ①2 3

3. [We are planning to go,] but [we may not

   arrive] [until the second half begins.]   1 2 ③

4. [City workers struck] [when they didn't get

   a raise.]   1 ②3

5. [He runs and bats well,] but [he can't catch

   the ball.]   1 ②3

*6. [Although we have little money,] [we are happy.]   1 ②3

Note: 6. Remember that an adverb can modify an adjective.

73

WORKSHEET 70

Count subject-verb combinations. Bracket all clauses. Identify subordinating conjunctions (S.C.) and draw arrows from adverb clauses to the words they modify.

*tricky sentences

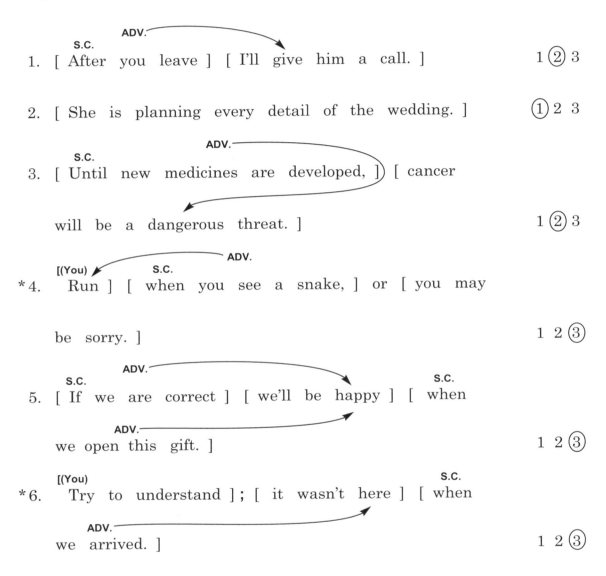

1. [After you leave] [I'll give him a call.]   1 ② 3

2. [She is planning every detail of the wedding.]   ① 2 3

3. [Until new medicines are developed,] [cancer

    will be a dangerous threat.]   1 ② 3

*4. Run] [when you see a snake,] or [you may

    be sorry.]   1 2 ③

5. [If we are correct] [we'll be happy] [when

    we open this gift.]   1 2 ③

*6. Try to understand] ; [it wasn't here] [when

    we arrived.]   1 2 ③

Notes: 4 and 6. There are two independent clauses in these sentences.

74

WORKSHEET 71

Put brackets around all clauses. Identify subordinating conjunctions. Draw arrows from adverb clauses to the words they modify. Remember that coordinating conjunctions which connect clauses are left <u>outside</u> the brackets.

*tricky sentences

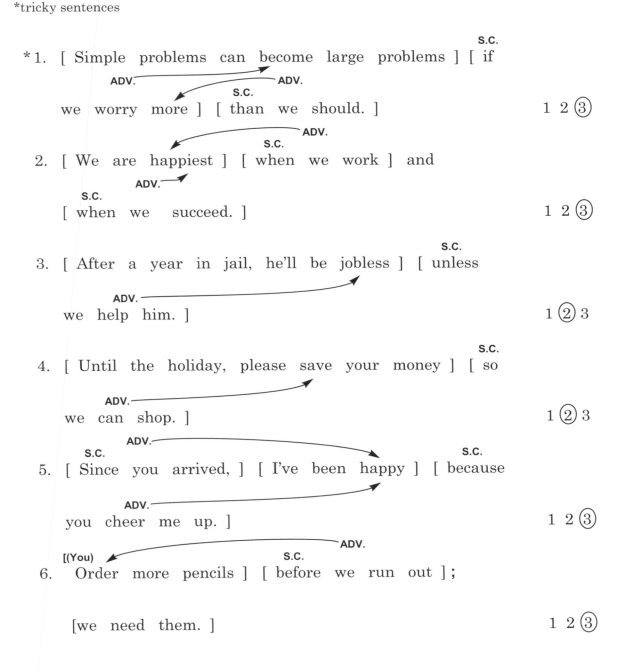

*1. [Simple problems can become large problems] [if
        we worry more] [than we should.]   1 2 ③

2. [We are happiest] [when we work] and
     [when we succeed.]   1 2 ③

3. [After a year in jail, he'll be jobless] [unless
    we help him.]   1 ② 3

4. [Until the holiday, please save your money] [so
    we can shop.]   1 ② 3

5. [Since you arrived,] [I've been happy] [because
    you cheer me up.]   1 2 ③

6. [(You) Order more pencils] [before we run out];

   [we need them.]   1 2 ③

Note: 1. **More** is an adverb modifying **worry; than we should** enlarges our understanding of **more**.

WORKSHEET 72

Count subject-verb combinations. Bracket all clauses. Identify adjective clauses. Mark relative pronouns (**R.P.**) and subordinating conjunctions (**S.C.**). Draw arrows to words modified.

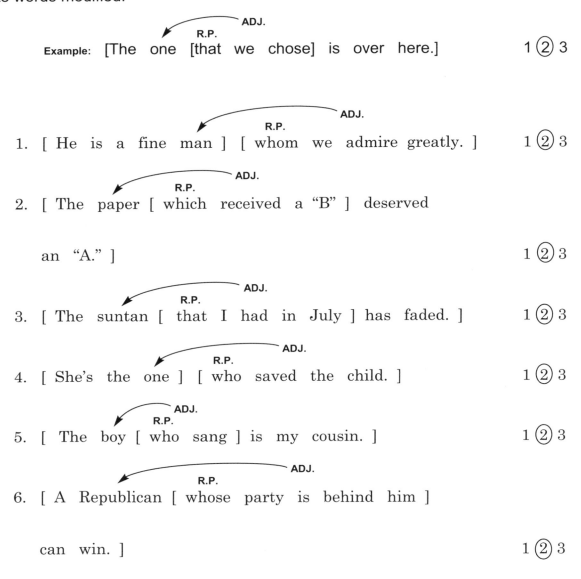

Example: [The one [that we chose] is over here.]   1 ②3

1. [He is a fine man] [whom we admire greatly.]   1 ②3

2. [The paper [which received a "B"] deserved

an "A."]   1 ②3

3. [The suntan [that I had in July] has faded.]   1 ②3

4. [She's the one] [who saved the child.]   1 ②3

5. [The boy [who sang] is my cousin.]   1 ②3

6. [A Republican [whose party is behind him]

can win.]   1 ②3

WORKSHEET 73

Count subject-verb combinations. Bracket all clauses. Identify adjective and adverb clauses. Mark relative pronouns (R.P.) and subordinating conjunctions (S.C.). Draw arrows to words modified.

*tricky sentences

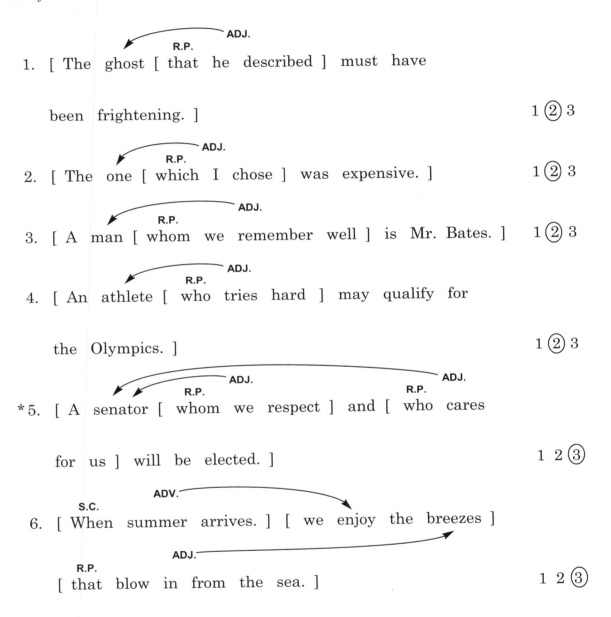

1. [The ghost [that he described] must have been frightening.]   1 ②3

2. [The one [which I chose] was expensive.]   1 ②3

3. [A man [whom we remember well] is Mr. Bates.]   1 ②3

4. [An athlete [who tries hard] may qualify for the Olympics.]   1 ②3

*5. [A senator [whom we respect] and [who cares for us] will be elected.]   1 2 ③

6. [When summer arrives.] [we enjoy the breezes] [that blow in from the sea.]   1 2 ③

Note: 5. Two dependent clauses are joined by a coordinating conjunction; both modify the subject of the independent clause.

WORKSHEET 74

Identify all clauses and mark them accordingly. Put **S.C.** above all subordinating conjunctions, and put **R.P.** above all relative pronouns. Watch out for relative pronouns which are not expressed. Put them in parentheses **( )**.

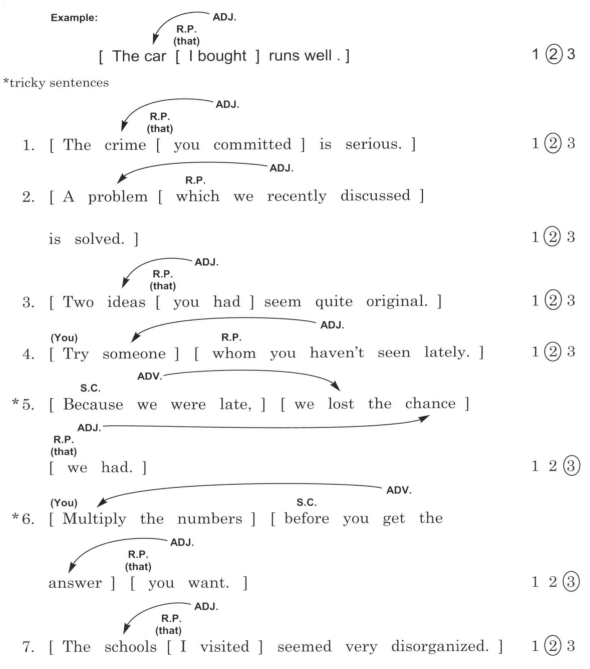

Example:

ADJ.
R.P.
(that)

[The car [I bought] runs well .]   1 ②3

*tricky sentences

ADJ.
R.P.
(that)

1. [The crime [you committed] is serious.]   1 ②3

ADJ.
R.P.

2. [A problem [which we recently discussed]

is solved.]   1 ②3

ADJ.
R.P.
(that)

3. [Two ideas [you had] seem quite original.]   1 ②3

ADJ.
(You)   R.P.

4. [Try someone] [whom you haven't seen lately.]   1 ②3

ADV.
S.C.

*5. [Because we were late,] [we lost the chance]

ADJ.
R.P.
(that)
[we had.]   1 2 ③

ADV.
(You)   S.C.

*6. [Multiply the numbers] [before you get the

ADJ.
R.P.
(that)
answer] [you want.]   1 2 ③

ADJ.
R.P.
(that)

7. [The schools [I visited] seemed very disorganized.]   1 ②3

Notes: 5. **We lost... because we were late**; this is an adverbial clause.
6. **Multiply... before you get the answer**; this is an adverbial clause.

78

WORKSHEET 75

Identify all clauses and mark them accordingly. Put **S.C.** above all subordinating conjunctions, and put **R.P.** above all relative pronouns. Watch out for relative pronouns which are not expressed. Put them in parentheses **( )**.

*tricky sentences

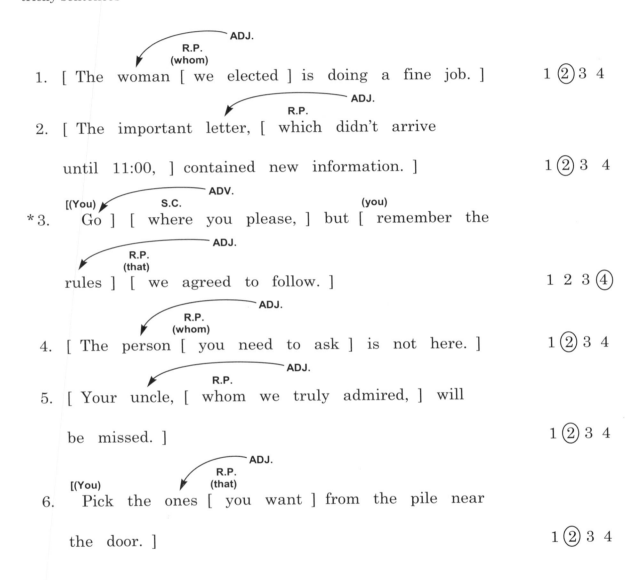

1. [The woman [we elected] is doing a fine job.]   1 ②3 4

2. [The important letter, [which didn't arrive

    until 11:00,] contained new information.]   1 ②3 4

*3.   Go] [where you please,] but [remember the

    rules] [we agreed to follow.]   1 2 3 ④

4. [The person [you need to ask] is not here.]   1 ②3 4

5. [Your uncle, [whom we truly admired,] will

    be missed.]   1 ②3 4

6.   Pick the ones [you want] from the pile near

    the door.]   1 ②3 4

Note: 3. **You go... You remember...** both are independent clauses joined by a c.c.

79

WORKSHEET 76

Bracket only dependent clauses. Label adverb and adjective clauses; identify words modified by drawing arrows. Label relative pronouns and subordinating conjunctions. Draw a circle around each noun clause or noun which acts as a direct object.

*tricky sentences

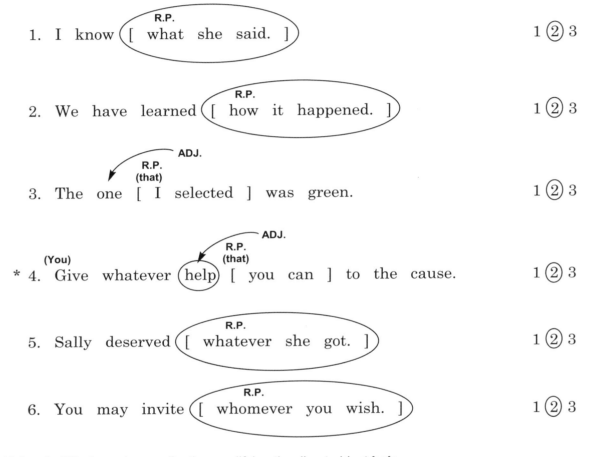

1. I know ([what she said.])   R.P.   1 ② 3

2. We have learned ([how it happened.])   R.P.   1 ② 3

3. The one [I selected] was green.   ADJ. R.P. (that)   1 ② 3

* 4. Give whatever (help) [you can] to the cause.   (You)   ADJ. R.P. (that)   1 ② 3

5. Sally deserved ([whatever she got.])   R.P.   1 ② 3

6. You may invite ([whomever you wish.])   R.P.   1 ② 3

Note: 4. **Whatever** is an adjective modifying the direct object **help**.

WORKSHEET 77

Bracket only dependent clauses. Label adverb and adjective clauses; identify words modified by drawing arrows. Label relative pronouns and subordinating conjunctions. Draw a circle around each noun clause which acts as a direct object.

*tricky sentences

(You)   ADJ.
                          R.P.
1. Put the jacket [that got wet] in the dryer.   1 ② 3

                              R.P.
2. The police asked ([why she did it.])   1 ② 3

                                R.P.
3. I don't remember ([which boy did it.])   1 ② 3

                          R.P.
4. We tried ([what seemed most logical.])   1 ② 3

                      R.P.
5. I realized ([who it was.])   1 ② 3

                          R.P.
* 6. Don't tell me ([how the movie ends.])   1 ② 3

Note: 6. **Me** is an indirect object between the action verb and the direct object clause.

81

WORKSHEET 78

Bracket dependent clauses. Label and draw arrows for adjective and adverb clauses. Noun clauses should be marked for function: circle direct objects, box indirect objects. Mark subordinating conjunctions and relative pronouns.

*tricky sentences

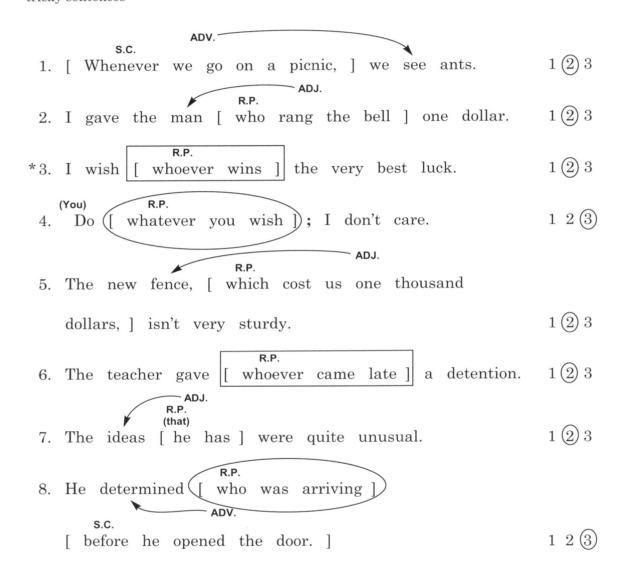

1. [Whenever we go on a picnic,] we see ants.   1 ② 3

2. I gave the man [who rang the bell] one dollar.   1 ② 3

*3. I wish [whoever wins] the very best luck.   1 ② 3

4. Do ([whatever you wish]); I don't care.   1 2 ③

5. The new fence, [which cost us one thousand

   dollars,] isn't very sturdy.   1 ② 3

6. The teacher gave [whoever came late] a detention.   1 ② 3

7. The ideas [he has] were quite unusual.   1 ② 3

8. He determined ([who was arriving]

   [before he opened the door.]   1 2 ③

Note: 3. **Luck** is the direct object; **whoever wins** comes between the action verb and the direct object.

WORKSHEET 79

Bracket all dependent clauses and label them. Noun clauses include direct objects, indirect objects, and <u>predicate nominatives</u>. Label relative pronouns R.P. and subordinating conjunctions S.C.

*tricky sentences

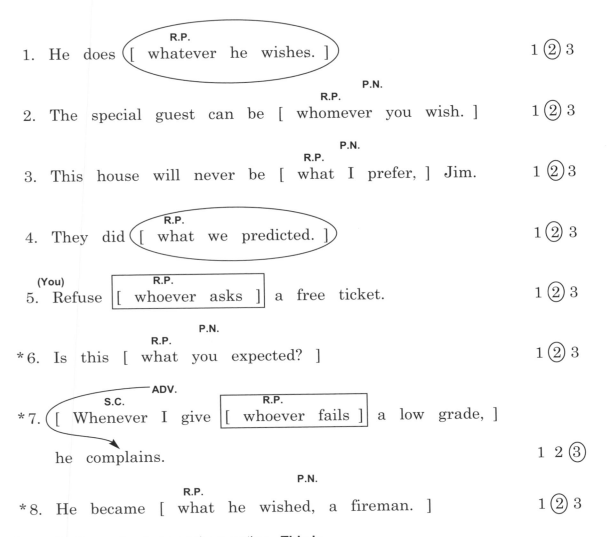

1. He does ([whatever he wishes.])   1 ② 3

2. The special guest can be [whomever you wish.]   1 ② 3

3. This house will never be [what I prefer,] Jim.   1 ② 3

4. They did ([what we predicted.])   1 ② 3

5. Refuse |[whoever asks]| a free ticket.   1 ② 3

*6. Is this [what you expected?]   1 ② 3

*7. ([Whenever I give |[whoever fails]| a low grade,]

he complains.   1 2 ③

*8. He became [what he wished, a fireman.]   1 ② 3

Notes: 6. Remember to invert the question-- **This is …**
7. The independent clause is **he complains**. **Whoever fails** is the indirect object of the adverbial dependent clause.
8. **Fireman** is an appositive naming **what he wished**. An appositive always names the noun that comes before it and is most often set off by commas. This is why the independent clause is not **He became a fireman** with **what he wished** as an appositive.

83

WORKSHEET 80

Bracket and label all dependent clauses and relative pronouns. These sentences include noun clauses functioning as objects of prepositions.

*tricky sentences

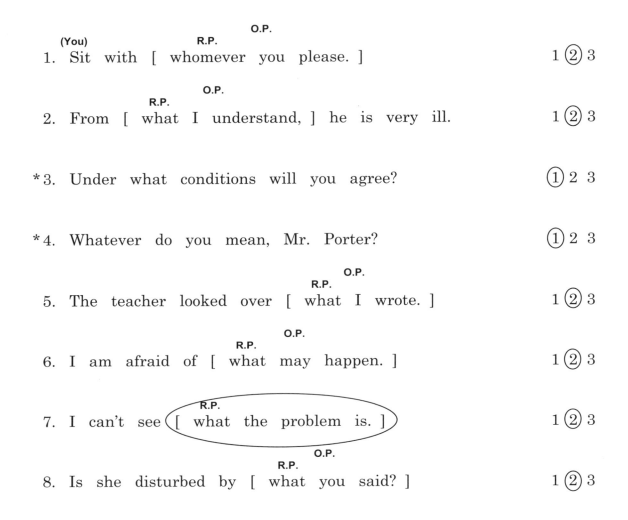

           (You)   R.P.   O.P.

1. Sit with [whomever you please.]   1 ② 3

                R.P.   O.P.

2. From [what I understand,] he is very ill.   1 ② 3

*3. Under what conditions will you agree?   ① 2 3

*4. Whatever do you mean, Mr. Porter?   ① 2 3

                 R.P. O.P.

5. The teacher looked over [what I wrote.]   1 ② 3

             R.P. O.P.

6. I am afraid of [what may happen.]   1 ② 3

            R.P.

7. I can't see ([what the problem is.])   1 ② 3

            R.P. O.P.

8. Is she disturbed by [what you said?]   1 ② 3

Notes: 3. **What conditions** has no subject-verb combination, so **what** is an adjective while **conditions** is the O.P.

      4. When the question is inverted, it becomes **You do mean whatever**. **Whatever** is not an R.P.

84

WORKSHEET 81

Bracket and label all dependent clauses, relative pronouns, and subordinating conjunctions. These sentences may include noun clauses functioning as appositives.

*tricky sentences

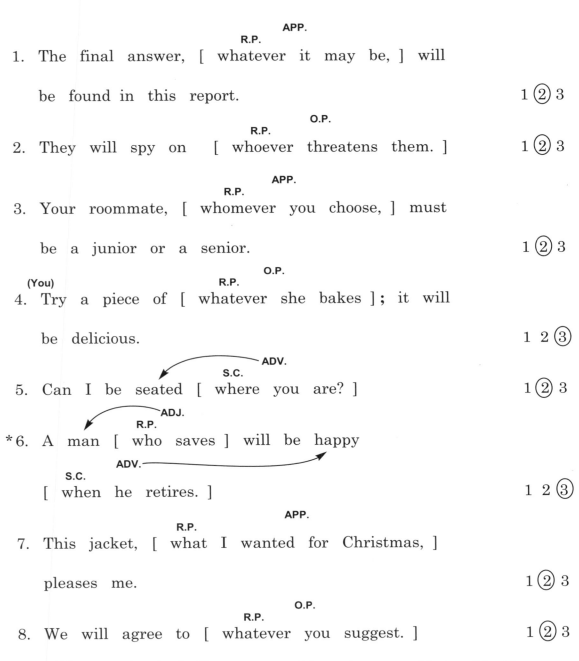

1. The final answer, [**APP.** **R.P.** whatever it may be,] will

   be found in this report. 1 ②3

2. They will spy on [**O.P.** **R.P.** whoever threatens them.] 1 ②3

3. Your roommate, [**APP.** **R.P.** whomever you choose,] must

   be a junior or a senior. 1 ②3

4. (You) Try a piece of [**O.P.** **R.P.** whatever she bakes]; it will

   be delicious. 1 2 ③

5. Can I be seated [**ADV.** **S.C.** where you are?] 1 ②3

*6. A man [**ADJ.** **R.P.** who saves] will be happy

   [**ADV.** **S.C.** when he retires.] 1 2 ③

7. This jacket, [**APP.** **R.P.** what I wanted for Christmas,]

   pleases me. 1 ②3

8. We will agree to [**O.P.** **R.P.** whatever you suggest.] 1 ②3

Note: 6. **Who saves** is not set off by commas nor it is naming **a man**; it is describing him.

85

WORKSHEET 82

Bracket and label all dependent clauses, relative pronouns, and subordinating conjunctions. These sentences may include noun clauses functioning as subjects.

*tricky sentences

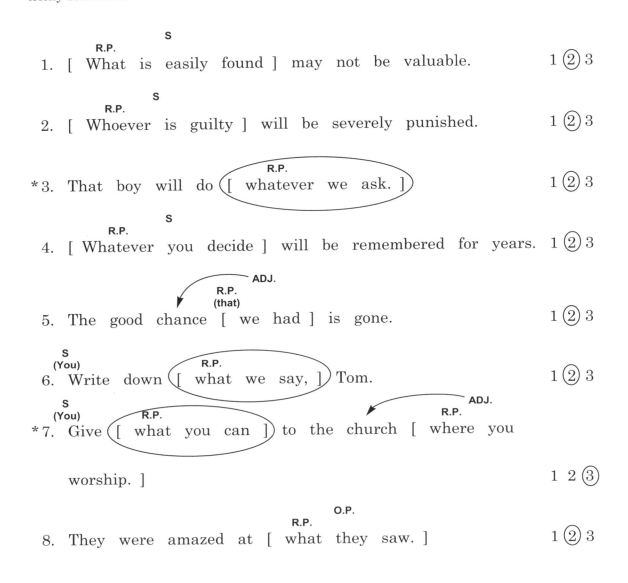

1.   [What is easily found] may not be valuable.   1 ② 3

        R.P.   S

2.   [Whoever is guilty] will be severely punished.   1 ② 3

*3. That boy will do ([whatever we ask.])   1 ② 3

4.   [Whatever you decide] will be remembered for years. 1 ② 3

5.   The good chance [we had] is gone.   1 ② 3

6.   Write down ([what we say,]) Tom.   1 ② 3

*7. Give ([what you can]) to the church [where you

      worship.]   1 2 ③

8.   They were amazed at [what they saw.]   1 ② 3

Notes: 3. **That** is an adjective describing **boy** not an R.P.
         7. The independent clause is **(You) give to the church**. Students might not see that the prepositional phrase is part of the independent clause.

WORKSHEET 83

Label and bracket all dependent clauses, relative pronouns and subordinating conjunctions.

*tricky sentences

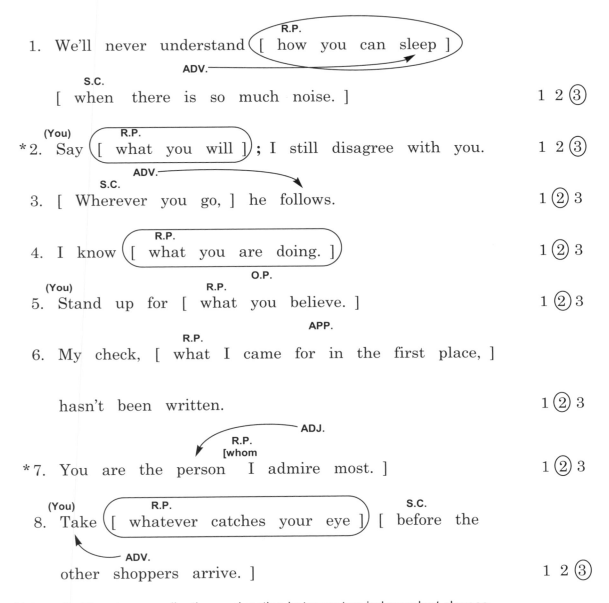

1. We'll never understand (**R.P.** [how you can sleep])
   ADV.
   S.C.
   [when there is so much noise.]   1 2 ③

*2. **(You)** Say (**R.P.** [what you will]); I still disagree with you.   1 2 ③
   ADV.
   S.C.
3. [Wherever you go,] he follows.   1 ② 3

4. I know (**R.P.** [what you are doing.])   1 ② 3
   O.P.
5. **(You)** Stand up for [**R.P.** what you believe.]   1 ② 3
   APP.
6. My check, [**R.P.** what I came for in the first place,]

   hasn't been written.   1 ② 3
   ADJ.
   R.P.
   [whom
*7. You are the person I admire most.]   1 ② 3

8. **(You)** Take (**R.P.** [whatever catches your eye]) **S.C.** [before the

   ADV.
   other shoppers arrive.]   1 2 ③

Notes: 2. The ; is a coordinating conjunction between two independent clauses.
      7. **Whom I admire most** is not set off by commas (like the clause in sentence 6) and doesn't name **the person**, but describes him/her, so is an adjective.

87

WORKSHEET 84

Label and bracket all dependent clauses, relative pronouns and subordinating conjunctions.
All of these are tricky!

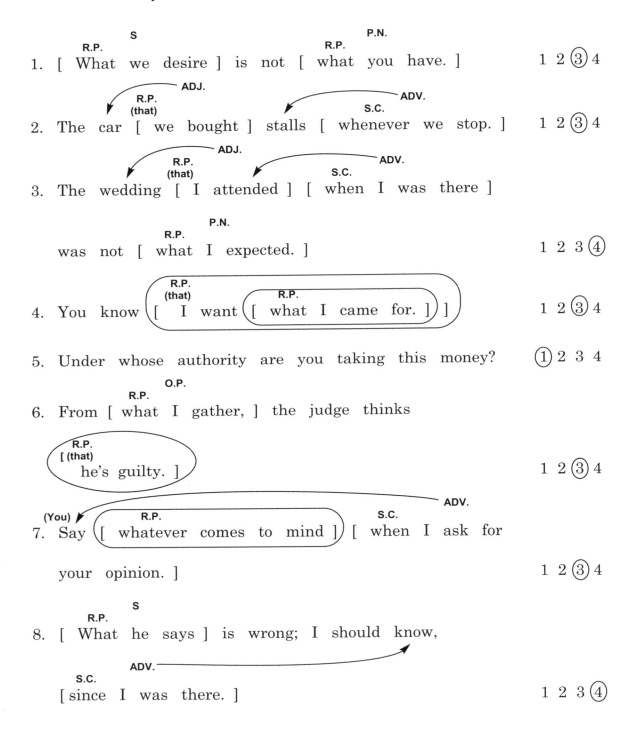

1. [What we desire] is not [what you have.]   1 2 ③ 4

2. The car [we bought] stalls [whenever we stop.]   1 2 ③ 4

3. The wedding [I attended] [when I was there]

    was not [what I expected.]   1 2 3 ④

4. You know ([I want ([what I came for.])])   1 2 ③ 4

5. Under whose authority are you taking this money?   ① 2 3 4

6. From [what I gather,] the judge thinks

    he's guilty.]   1 2 ③ 4

7. Say ([whatever comes to mind]) [when I ask for

    your opinion.]   1 2 ③ 4

8. [What he says] is wrong; I should know,

    [since I was there.]   1 2 3 ④

88

WORKSHEET 85

Label and bracket all dependent clauses, relative pronouns and subordinating conjunctions.
All of these are extra-tricky!

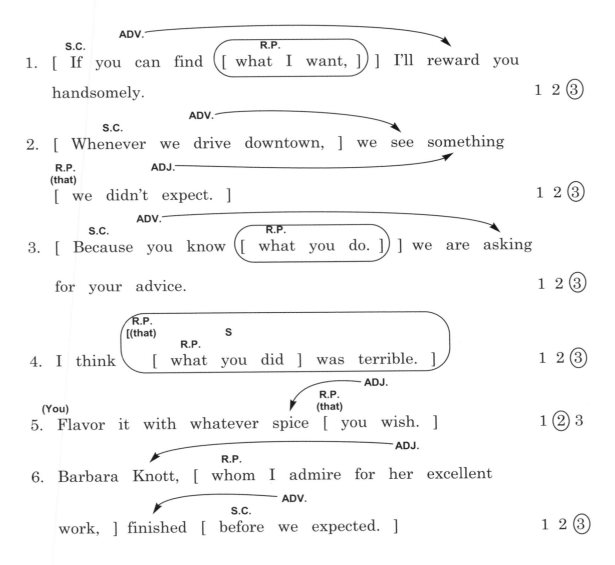

1. [If you can find [what I want,]] I'll reward you handsomely.　　　　　1 2 ③

2. [Whenever we drive downtown,] we see something [we didn't expect.]　　　　　1 2 ③

3. [Because you know [what you do.]] we are asking for your advice.　　　　　1 2 ③

4. I think [what you did] was terrible.]　　　　　1 2 ③

5. Flavor it with whatever spice [you wish.]　　　　　1 ② 3

6. Barbara Knott, [whom I admire for her excellent work,] finished [before we expected.]　　　　　1 2 ③

QUIZ -- Lessons 41-52

Identify all nouns and pronouns. Indicate noun functions. Label all adjectives and adverbs, and draw arrows to words modified.

          adv.   S
                     pron.   N.D.A.

1. Where are you, Fred?

      adj.   S
            P.N.   pron.   O.P.

2. What time is it in Chicago?

       S   S
      pron.   adj.   pron.   adv.

3. This is fine, but that won't do.

    S
  pron.   O.P.
  (You)   pron.   pron.   O.P.

4. Help yourself to some of the candy.

     adv.   S   adj.

5. When will the Mayor make his decision?

    adv.   S
            pron.

6. Where is mine?

    adv.   S
        adv. pron.   pron.   O.P.

7. Why doesn't he make himself a cup of coffee?

   S
 pron.   O.P.   adv.

8. Who will clean the gym after the game tonight?

QUIZ -- Lessons 41-62

Identify all nouns and pronouns. Mark noun functions. Label all adjectives and adverbs. Draw arrows to words modified. Watch out for participles, infinitives. and gerunds.

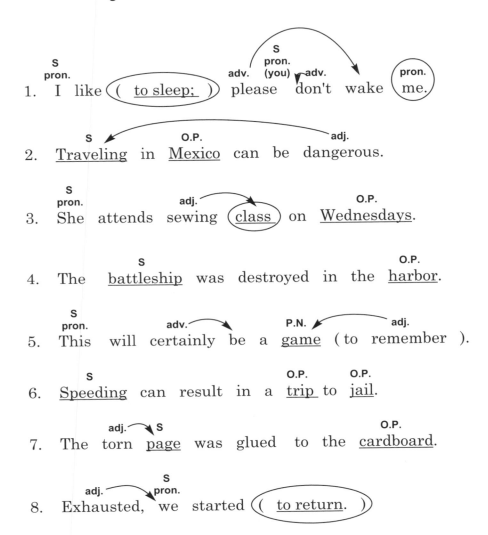

1. I like (to sleep;) please don't wake me.

2. Traveling in Mexico can be dangerous.

3. She attends sewing (class) on Wednesdays.

4. The battleship was destroyed in the harbor.

5. This will certainly be a game (to remember).

6. Speeding can result in a trip to jail.

7. The torn page was glued to the cardboard.

8. Exhausted, we started ((to return.))

QUIZ -- Lessons 41-71

Count subject-verb combinations in each sentence. Bracket all clauses.
Identify subordinating conjunctions. Label adverb clauses and draw arrows to
words modified.

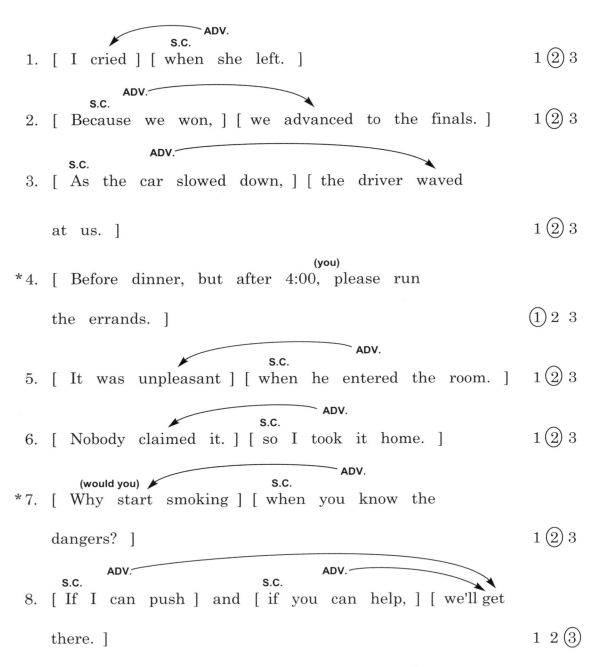

1. [I cried] [when she left.]   1 ②3

2. [Because we won,] [we advanced to the finals.]   1 ②3

3. [As the car slowed down,] [the driver waved

   at us.]   1 ②3

*4. [Before dinner, but after 4:00, please run
   (you)

   the errands.]   ①2 3

5. [It was unpleasant] [when he entered the room.]   1 ②3

6. [Nobody claimed it.] [so I took it home.]   1 ②3

*7. [Why start smoking] [when you know the
   (would you)

   dangers?]   1 ②3

8. [If I can push] and [if you can help,] [we'll get

   there.]   1 2 ③

Notes: 4. **Before dinner, after 4:00** are prepositional phrases, not clauses.
            7. The independent clause is **You would start smoking why.**

QUIZ -- Lessons 41-75

Bracket all clauses. Label dependent clauses **ADJ.** or **ADV..** Draw arrows to words modified. Label subordinating conjunctions **S.C.** and relative pronouns **R.P..**

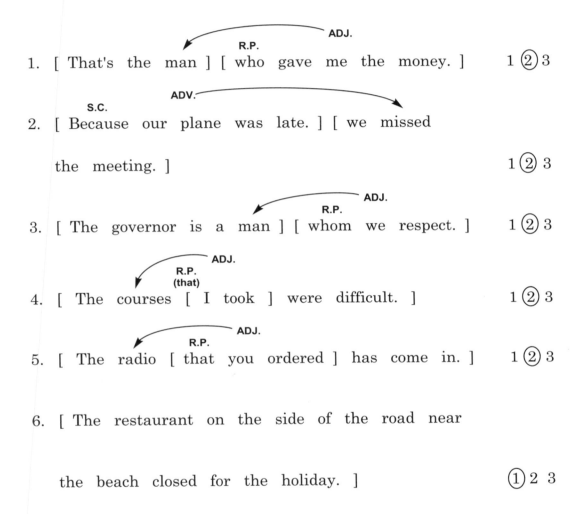

1. [That's the man] [who gave me the money.]   1 ②3

2. [Because our plane was late.] [we missed

    the meeting.]   1 ② 3

3. [The governor is a man] [whom we respect.]   1 ② 3

4. [The courses [I took] were difficult.]   1 ② 3

5. [The radio [that you ordered] has come in.]   1 ② 3

6. [The restaurant on the side of the road near

    the beach closed for the holiday.]   ① 2 3

QUIZ -- Lessons 41-79

Bracket all dependent clauses and identify their parts of speech. Label relative pronouns and subordinating conjunctions. Mark noun functions of clauses.

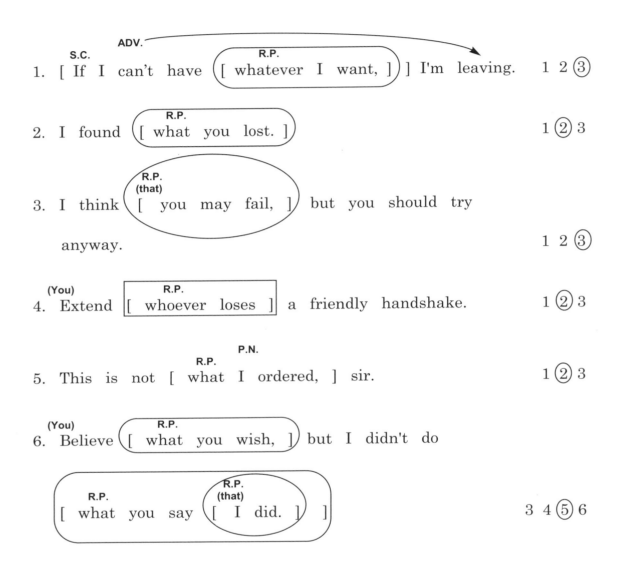

1. [If I can't have ([whatever I want,])] I'm leaving.   1 2 ③

2. I found ([what you lost.])   1 ② 3

3. I think ([you may fail,]) but you should try

   anyway.   1 2 ③

4. Extend [whoever loses] a friendly handshake.   1 ② 3

5. This is not [what I ordered,] sir.   1 ② 3

6. Believe ([what you wish,]) but I didn't do

   [what you say ([I did.])]   3 4 ⑤ 6